MASONIC MEMORABILIA

FOR COLLECTORS

BY

BILL JACKMAN

EDITED BY

GEORGE PERROTT

GEMINI PUBLICATIONS LTD

Published by Gemini Publications Ltd
30a Monmouth Street, Bath, BA1 2AN, England, UK.

Designed by: Larraine Lawrence
Jacket Design by: Larraine Lawrence
Photography by Photoreel

ISBN 0-9530637-2-0

Printed and Bound in the EU by Marks Print UK.

CONTENTS

PREFACE

This book has been written to fill an important gap in the antiques and collectables information market. I have been encouraged by both collectors and dealers, who have also given me their views on whether I should include prices. After discussion with the editor, George Perrott, it was decided to include them, because it is what most collectors want to know - the popularity of the BBC Antiques Road Show seems to prove this.

Little or nothing has been written on the values of Masonic artefacts, which makes this book even more valuable to the collector. I have diligently researched auction catalogues and acquired the opinions of many people in the trade who have checked through the valuations of this book to doubly check that they are very near to the current market prices.

The majority of the glass and china you will find in the book is part of my own collection, and most of it was bought from some of the best dealers in the country. I made sure that every piece was in pristine condition. I have also bought many pieces off the web.

As there are so many jewels to choose from I have listed what I consider to be the most collectable and easy to find; although I have also included some of the more expensive ones.

At the end of the book I have included a small section of Masonic collectables from Brother C.Clark Julius's collection. He is probably the greatest authority on Masonic memorabilia in America, who over the years has collected a vast assortment. He would be delighted to hear from English collectors.

I thank all persons who have helped me, most of whom are referred to in my acknowledgements. Happy hunting.

Bill Jackman

ACKNOWLEDGEMENTS AND CREDITS

Although the idea and the text were the efforts of the author, it would never have seen the light of day without a certain amount of luck, and a lot of hard work by people who saw the potential in getting this book into print.

Firstly I must thank Diana Cambridge, the editor of *Antique & Collectables Magazine*, for her suggestion that I contact my Partner and Editor, George Perrott, and despite the adage that there are no friends in business I have taken to him as a colleague and friend. (That's the luck side I mentioned).

Wendy, his wife, has been a constant source of support, with a steady supply of tea and sandwiches as we often worked into the dark hours of night. Then, when we were resting, she would proof read and re-type.

I thank Diane Hollands who has written the index for us, and also proof read.

Charles Cornish who has been a great help in ensuring the technical details were correct, particularly in respect of the jewels.

Mike Pettitt of Roland Gallery, 33 Monmouth Street, Bath, for his expert help in checking through some of the valuations.

Poole Masonic Museum, in particular Peter Marks the curator and Bill Williams his assistant, who allowed us a free hand in photographing many items which are included in this book, and assisting us with valuations.

Mark Dennis, the curator of the Museum at the Masonic Hall, Great Queen Street, London, for his help and support.

My friend, Des McGuinness, for allowing me to photograph his jewels.

From across the Atlantic Brother C.Clark Julius, an avid collector of everything Masonic, who has many books and has given me free hand to take valuable information from them.

I also thank W. Brother Terry Hart, the Assistant Provincial Grand Master of Somerset, for checking the Masonic history for correctness and accuracy.

Roger de Ville - who over the years has supplied me with most of my china and porcelain. I recommend him as he supplies top quality at reasonable prices.

Most of all my wife, family and friends who gave their encouragement and time to help me through this project.

Bill Jackman

Gemini Publications Ltd

Publishers

bookbasket

30a Monmouth Street, Bath, BA1 2AN, England, UK.

**LATEST BOOKLIST ON ANTIQUES & COLLECTABLES
FROM GEMINI PUBLICATIONS**

Telephone: 01225 484877 Fax: 01225 334619
Email bookbasket@btconnect.com
Web: www.bookbasket.co.uk

Retailers and wholesalers are welcome to apply for our special discounts

Masonic Memorabilia for Collectors.

By Bill Jackman. Edited by George Perrott.
This is the first book on Freemasonry artifacts to be published with a price guide. Packed with useful information with over 150 coloured illustrations. It covers china, glass, jewels of the craft, books, prints, etc., and gives tips on how to spot fakes; how to care for your collection and where to buy the best pieces.
Softback 240x170mm, 120 pages. ISBN 0-9530637-2-0
Price £17.95. To be published July/Aug 2002.

Complete Price Guide to Watches 2002.

By Cooksey Shugart, Tom Engle and Richard Gilbert.
This book is a simple reference with clear and carefully selected information. The first part is devoted to history and general information. The second part consists mainly of a listing of watch manufacturers, identification guides and prices. With the aid of this book, the collector should be able to make on-the-spot judgments.
Softback. 215x140mm. 1,134 pages. ISBN 1-57432-291-5
Price £29.95
PUBLISHED JANUARY 2002 AND IS AVAILABLE. (UK Agent)

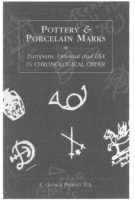

Pottery & Porcelain Marks, European, Oriental & USA.

By E.G.Perrott.
Commencing with the Ming Dynasty of 1368, through to the 15th century 'Maiolica' period of the Italian Renaissance, the German and French 'Faience' of the 16th century, the early 17th century Dutch 'Delft' wares, then onto the great factories of Europe, Meissen, Sevres, and the English factories of Wedgwood, Minton, etc., to the USA factories of the 18th & 19th centuries.
Hardback 250x175mm, 667 pages. ISBN 0-9530637-0-4
Price £45.00. PUBLISHED 1997. AVAILABLE.

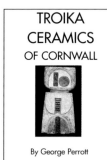

TROIKA CERAMICS OF CORNWALL

By George Perrott

Troika Ceramics of Cornwall.

By George Perrott.
History of the company and its products. With more than 150 coloured illustrations and lots of useful information covering the backstamps and marks, which includes the various designers who worked for Troika. Plus latest up-to-date price guide of this unique pottery.
Softback 240x170mm. 120 pages. ISBN 0-9530637-3-9
Price £17.95. TO BE PUBLISHED OCT/NOV 2002.

The policy of Gemini Publications is to publish at least four books per year specialising in antique and collectable subjects. We have 'Masonic Collectables' by Bill Jackman and 'Troika Ceramics' by George Perrott in the pipeline. Our eventual aim is to find those subjects that are interesting and collectable but of which there isn't much information, or alternately up-date those books on collectables that have overrun their shelf life.
If you are a potential writer with an idea on any collectable subject give us a call, we might be able to help you.

Distributed by Gemini Publications Ltd., 30A Monmouth Street, Bath, BA1 2AN, England.
Telephone: 01225 484877 Fax: 01225 334619.

INTRODUCTION

It is a strange phenomena that an institution as well established as Freemasonry, and for which thousands of pieces of commemorative ware have been manufactured over two hundred and fifty years or so, has little or nothing written to benefit the collector and assist in evaluating individual pieces, the history of them and where to find them.

I have searched through dozens of books on every aspect of Masonic memorabilia and despite the many collectors throughout the world, I have found nothing listing Masonic collectables as an entity in their own right. This will be partly corrected when the United Grand Lodge of England presents their new catalogue of exhibits in their museum.

It is interesting when looking through some of the earlier books on porcelain and china that the Creamware pots and jugs of the 18th century clearly show the transfer prints of a public house, or a sailor's farewell, but the picture on the reverse side, with Masonic symbols on it, is not given a mention. In fact on the blue and white mug, illustrated on Page 64, the Masonic tools and emblems are loosely referred to as a 'collection of tools' with no reference to them being Masonic.

The sign of the Freemasons is easily recognisable. Its basic emblem is a square and a pair of draughtsman compasses, one set on top of the other. There is sometimes a letter 'G' in the centre, which represents 'The Grand Geometrician of the Universe'. The compasses are always at the top of the diamond configuration and the square in the lower half.

Square and compass.

How it all began

It is believed that in or around the year 1118 a small group of French knights took on the supposed role of guarding the Christian pilgrims making their way to the Holy Land, but it seems their actual intention was to dig under the foundations of King Herod's Temple and try to recover the vast amount of wealth and other biblical treasures hidden there during the fall of Jerusalem and the destruction of the temple in AD 76. Beneath the temple were huge vaults used for storage and stabling, with acres of rooms, some with collapsed ceilings and walls. After years of tunnelling and digging, an untold amount of treasure was recovered, so much so that the Knights Templars became one of the richest sects in Europe. Over the years their numbers increased and they accumulated a vast quantity of land and castles throughout Europe. They became very powerful; Kings and Bishops and indeed the different Popes held them in respect for their power and wealth and they were bankers to many European kings and churches.

In 1307, King Philip IV of France needed money very badly. Even though the King had received generous sums from the Templars, he organised his own man as Pope and convinced him that the Templars were a threat to the Vatican and the security of France and Europe and should be excommunicated. The King planned a top secret plot and on Friday 13th October, 1307 it was put into effect. To justify his accusations he rounded up 1,500 Templars and put them into dungeons where they were tortured until confessions were extracted from them, vindicating the King's actions, which included seizing the Templars' treasure. Fortunately for some

It is interesting to add at this stage that, according to the Oxford English Dictionary, the definition of a Templar is: 'a member of a military and religious order, consisting of knights (Knights Templars, Knights of Poor Soldiers of the Temple), chaplains, and men-at-arms, founded c1118, chiefly for the protection of the Holy Sepulchre (the cave in which Jesus Christ was buried) and of Christian pilgrims visiting the Holy Land; so called from their occupation of a building on or near the site of the Temple of Solomon at Jerusalem. They were suppressed in 1312'.

Rosslyn Chapel, the 15th century Chapel, seven miles south of Edinburgh, is one of Scotland's most beautiful and historic churches, renowned for its world-famous carvings.
Courtesy of Antonia Reeve/Rosslyn Chapel Trust.

of the Templars, the secret orders issued by the King leaked out and some of them managed to escape from France, taking with them most of the vast wealth of the Templars in their fleet of ships. The eventual whereabouts of the fleet was never discovered, although their infamous battle flag the 'skull and crossbones' was adopted as the ensign of various marauding pirates and buccaneers.

It is thought that the fleet split in two, and one half made for la Merica (America) and the other half for Scotland, via Ireland. The Pope had ordered that no sanctuary should be given to these Knights in Europe and that they should be killed or imprisoned if found. They were, however, befriended by Robert The Bruce who had also been excommunicated by the Pope, so had nothing to lose in helping them.

There is no evidence that the Knights Templars did land in America, but there is a strong belief that they may have done, and a long time before Christopher Columbus arrived there. Rosslyn Castle and Rosslyn Chapel were designed and built by St Clair, a Scottish Knight Templar, who having given great service to Robert The Bruce, was rewarded with land south of Edinburgh. The building work was completed 40 years before Columbus landed in America. The interior of the chapel shows ears of corn, or 'Indian maize' as it was known, carved into the stonework, and as this was a plant not known in Britain until nearly 100 years later, it is more than a possibility that the only way the builders of the chapel could have known of the corn plant is by fellow Templars travelling to and from America.

William St Clair III had at his disposal, and it would appear in trust, the residue of the Templars' religious relics and wealth. The interior of Rosslyn Chapel has, in its many carvings and mouldings, the mystic stories of the ancient Christian readings. The Chapel is believed to be a shrine to The Knights Templars. Every carving has significance to Templars and one can see the links to Freemasonry. The Chapel is well worth a visit and has been well documented.

The mysteries of Rosslyn Chapel remain to this day and will continue until the caretakers of the Chapel allow the vaults to be excavated and the Templars' secrets revealed. The actual birth of Freemasonry, from the decline of the Knights Templars in Scotland, is yet to be fully explained and researched, but one could imagine a new breed of brotherhood based on the rituals of Templars may have developed from the Stonemasons that built Rosslyn Chapel.

During this period there were guilds of different trades, for example the Gold and Silversmiths, the Armourers and the Stonemasons. Many other guilds followed. The Stonemasons had great skills, and were called upon to build classical and enduring cathedrals, castles, stately homes and palaces. They travelled the country and were in great demand, indeed as were the Masons of other countries - France and Germany developed Freemasonry at the same time. These were men who learned the trade to fashion stone so that it fitted perfectly, one piece into another, their skill enabling them to convert a quarried lump of raw material into a work of extreme beauty, one that would last for a thousand years. The skills of these master craftsmen, which had taken generations to learn, were not passed on to anyone lightly. They had to be learnt by their apprentices over many years. As they improved new secrets were released to them which they, in turn, cherished and only disclosed to those who followed in the trade. It is no different today; one wouldn't expect a top chef to disclose secrets of how he produces such wonderful food and sauces - a technique he has acquired over many years - to an unqualified person, until perhaps they have proved their worth.

It therefore follows that as these bands of travelling Masons went from town to town, lodges of accommodation and training schools for apprentices were established throughout the country. It took many men to build a cathedral and a lot of skill was required by the Stonemasons.

When one looks at the wonderful art of the Stonemasons, one can see that years of training by tied apprentices were needed to reach such a standard. If a master Mason was training a pupil he would want to make sure that, following training, the pupil would remain an employee. He was therefore tied to his master. My own interpretation is that the Stonemason Guild in Britain could have been the basic breeding ground to form lodges of men who worked, lived and trained together and possibly incorporating into their rituals traditions once used by The Knights Templars in a brotherhood of Masonic secrets.

I hope that this brief history of how Freemasonry was possibly born from the days of The Knights Templars will help to illustrate the vast worldwide brotherhood that it has become.

THE DIFFERENCES BETWEEN THE MODERNS AND THE ANCIENTS

There are many Freemasons to whom the term Ancients and Moderns is a little confusing. This is even more understandable when the facts are that the Ancients came after the Moderns. The Most Ancient and Honourable Society of Free and Accepted Masons was founded in London in 1751. It had very small beginnings and consisted of only six lodges made up of about eighty brothers. It was not by any means the first Grand Lodge, but a breakaway from what already existed. It disapproved of alterations that were made to ritual, and the forbidding of processions which the Moderns had abolished in 1743. This new group, the Ancients, wanted to keep to the old ways and not follow the trend of the Moderns. They were not known as Moderns at the time; this was a term adopted by Laurence Dermott who took pride in calling his Grand Lodge, The Ancients, and the former Grand Lodge, The Moderns.

The brethren who formed the Ancients were not of the usual upper class group from society but from the lower grade of professional men. They were mainly craftsmen of low incomes such as tailors, painters, shoemakers and shopkeepers. Many of them were Irish or had Irish connections. Laurence Dermott became their Grand Secretary in 1752 and held the post until 1771. He became Deputy Grand Master that year. He was well educated and compiled the first book of Constitutions, *Ahimon Rezon*. This was published in 1756 and was the first Book of Constitutions of the new Grand Lodge. The Ancients took pride in the old system, and because of this habit of conducting themselves in ancient ways were soon known as the 'Ancients'. The new order accommodated lodges further afield, The Grand Lodge in London became remote and seldom visited.

There were the military lodges; many Regiments had their own lodges which travelled the world with them. These found the new break-away Grand Lodge more in keeping with their needs. It was in the Grand Lodge of Ancients that the Holy Royal Arch was formed. The Royal Arch had not been recognised by the Moderns until the amalgamation in 1813.

The Grand Lodges of Scotland and Ireland had little time for Premier Grand Lodge (The Moderns). They held the Ancients in high regard and admired their Masonic attitudes to Freemasonry. The Ancients were not accepted by the Moderns and their members were told not to fraternise with them. There were heavy penalties imposed on those Masons who ignored this directive. The Scottish and Irish lodges, however, ignored this instruction.

In the later part of the 18th century Ancient Lodges were called ATHOLL LODGES because the various Dukes of Atholl were continually filling the chair of Grand Master. The two Grand Lodges were amalgamated in 1813 to become The Grand Lodge of England.

The history of the Ancients and Moderns is particularly interesting to collectors because you can distinguish early items by their symbols; the Ancients and Moderns had separate emblems. They both used the Square and Compasses emblem but only the Ancients used the Royal Arch symbol. This means that items dating prior to the amalgamation will have distinguishing symbols on them. This will be of particular interest to collectors of early jewels of the Holy Royal Arch especially the pierced ones dating between 1790-1820. Early glass and china objects made during 1751- 1813 also show the difference between Ancients, whose emblems included the Royal Arch design and the Moderns who did not.

FREEMASONRY IN ENGLAND

The Goose and Gridiron Alehouse, the first meeting place of Grand Lodge, 24 June 1717.
Artist's impression based on a sketch published in 1894 when the building was demolished.

Freemasonry and the strict codes in England, under the auspices of The Grand Lodge of England, vary in many parts of the world, where ethical and political standards are not so strict; nevertheless there are thousands of lodges throughout the world that are recognised by The Grand Lodge of England.

In England it is a basic requirement that every brother has to believe in a God (one of his own choosing). However, politics and religion are forbidden subjects of discussion by the brethren in lodges. It is not a secret society, neither is it a society of secrets, and neither is it a religion. It is a society that practice Brotherly Love, Relief and Truth and raises large sums of money for charity from the members within the confines of the lodge premises.

The brotherhood has nearly three hundred years of history behind it and is spread worldwide. This means that wherever one goes in the world there is a chance of finding some piece of memorabilia allied to some form of Freemasonry.

While it is accepted that many readers of this book will already have more than a basic knowledge of Freemasonry, this is an ideal opportunity to enlighten the uninitiated collectors as to where it actually began in England.

Freemasonry was fragmented in its early days and although many wanted to be members there was no proper organisation, only groups meeting in various places. The first acknowledged meeting house of Freemasons as a collective group of like-minded brothers was in a pub in London called The Goose and Gridiron. This is where The Grand Lodge was first formed on 21st June, 1717. The pub was demolished in 1894 but once stood in an area now known as Paternoster Square. For the first 60 years of existence The Grand Lodge had no regular building for its meetings, and used many different pubs and assembly rooms. It met in numerous halls but it was at the Merchant Tailors' Hall that the first official Minutes of a Grand Lodge meeting were held in 1723. Even though it took many years to decide, it eventually became obvious that Freemasonry and the Grand Lodge should have their own buildings. The first Freemasons Hall, actually dedicated as such, was in Great Queen Street, London. The premises were purchased for £3,150.

In 1789 the Hall was rebuilt. A picture of how it looked then is on the giant meat platter shown on page 65.

The front of the building was a tavern and the gardens at the rear converted to the first Freemasons Hall. It was used mainly as assembly rooms and was let out for private functions to the public. It was not until the amalgamation of the Ancients and the Moderns, in 1813, that the Hall became designed and officially recognised as the Grand Temple. There was a fire in 1883 which meant the buildings and rooms had to be redesigned. The Connaught Rooms in Great Queen Street (shown adjacent to Freemasons Hall on the large meat platter) still exist today, and it is these that were once

The Masonic Million
Memorial Fund
Commemorative Jewel
(shown without collar
ribbons).
Estimate: £30-40 ($45-60)

known as Freemasons Tavern.

In 1932 it became obvious that the old Masonic Hall was beginning to crumble and would require a vast amount of money to put right. There now was a need for a much larger and up-to-date hall on the same ground. This would be the third hall. It was a very ambitious project, and involved pulling down the old building, a complete redesign and rebuild. To help raise the million pounds needed for the project, a special jewel was struck which a brother could purchase for £10 - he was then entitled to wear it in his craft lodge. It had the grand title of The Masonic Million Memorial Fund Commemorative Jewel. The jewel is described as "in the form of a cross, symbolising sacrifice, with a perfect square at the four ends, on the left and right square being dates 1914-1918, the years in which the supreme sacrifice was made. Between these is the winged figure of Peace presenting the representation of a Temple of special Masonic allusion in the Pillars, Porch and Steps. The medal is suspended by the Square and Compasses, attached to a ribbon, the whole thus symbolising the Craft's gift of a Temple in memory of those brethren who gave all for King and Country, Peace and Victory." These jewels are collectable and there are still plenty to be found.

The Hall Stone Jewel.
Estimate: £90-120 ($135-180)

Hall Stone Jewel

Another much larger jewel to exactly the same design, was donated to individual Craft Lodges who had subscribed in their voluntary donations an equivalent of £10 per head to the Memorial Fund. These jewels, which were presented to the Lodge not to an individual, are still worn by the Master of the Lodge during his year of office and then passed on to the next incoming Master. They are called the Hall Stone Jewels. This jewel is very much a collector's piece and is far more valuable than the smaller individual Commemorative Jewel.

THOMAS HARPER

Thomas Harper was a very famous Freemason. He was born in 1735 and was initiated into Freemasonry in 1761. It was into Lodge 24 that his long and distinguished career began. This lodge was situated in Bush Inn, Marsh Street, Bristol, where he made rapid progress due to his unflinching desire to further Freemasonry, which was still in its infancy. This resulted in him becoming the first Junior Warden of Lodge 190. He was later honoured as Grand Lodge Officer under the Atholl Register when aged 50.

He became treasurer of Grand Lodge in 1794, an office he served with dedication. He joined many different lodges during his lifetime, learning and teaching the benefits and aspirations of Freemasonry. He knew that if it were to survive, drastic measures had to be taken to amalgamate the Ancients and Moderns and to regulate the ritual and degrees which would be carried into the next century and beyond.

The sudden death in Grand Lodge of William Dickie resulted in Thomas Harper taking his place as Deputy Grand Master. He served Craft Masonry with great distinction and his knowledge of the craft and its history made him an authority, so much so that he was a main instigator of the amalgamation of the Ancients and Moderns and became one of the signatories in 1813 when the present day Freemasons were formed.

He was also a very skilled silversmith and his mark, which was registered in the Guild of Silversmiths in 1790, was of his initials TH set in a rectangle. He manufactured some of the first jewels. There are still some of his original jewels available to the collector but these are very sought after and would cost over £1,000 should they ever come on the market.

There is a lodge today called The Thomas Harper Lodge in memory of this great man who did so much for Freemasonry. It is about to celebrate its seventh year since being founded. It is open for any Mason to join but it is principally for collectors and Masonic researchers. It meets three times a year, once in the north of England, once in the south and all initiations are carried out in Birmingham. Thomas Harper died on 25th April 1832 at the ripe old age of 92. The Thomas Harper Lodge will ensure that his name, and what he stood, for will be remembered for many years to come.

FREEMASONS' HALL

Freemasons' Hall in Great Queen Street, London.
Photograph by kind permission of United Grand Lodge of England.

The Freemasons' Hall is a magnificent spacious building open to the public. It houses one of the finest libraries in the world, covering all aspects of Masonic matters, but is purely for reference and study. There is also a large museum of Masonic artefacts, dating back nearly 300 hundred years. It is interesting to see the Masonic items made by prisoners from the Napoleonic War; and those incarcerated in Germany during the First and Second World Wars and also those unfortunates under the Japanese in Changi Jail, Singapore. It shows how even under the harshest of conditions, men practiced and manufactured the jewels needed to perform Masonic ceremonies, making them out of any scraps of metal, paper or wood available.

Visitors are welcome to Freemasons' Hall, the entrance being in Great Queen Street, London. It is a monument in memory to those members who paid the supreme sacrifice in the First World-War - "they did not grow old - they gave their today for our tomorrow".

The most interesting area to the visitor is obviously the museum, which contains a massive collection of jewels, china, glass, regalia and other artefacts gathered over many years, mainly from England and its related lodges. On the dark polished wooden floor stand illuminated cabinets of silver, gold and other precious materials and collections from India and many other countries of the old British Empire. Also on display are a rich selection of pottery and porcelain ranging from the Meissen, Derby, Worcester, Coalport and Sunderland factories to the very rare Chinese export pieces of the Chi'en Lung period (1735-1795). In amongst all these desirable items there is a good collection of pieces that you will find detailed and valued within this book. But collectors must always be aware that many rare items will mostly only be seen in museums.

There is also a wonderful collection of glass, in all types of colourful and different designs including the famous Firing Glasses which you will find described in the Glass section of this book. Fine examples of enamelled glass said to be made by the famous maker and decorator William Beilby (1740-1819) can be seen here, and there is also a good selection of old Bristol Blue and Nailsea glass. Blue decanters extravagantly designed with painted Masonic symbols are also on display.

As well as china and glass there are cabinets filled with all sorts of interesting miscellaneous items which are made in less valuable materials, pieces like snuff and match boxes, watches, penknives, rings, pens, wallets, brooches and many other items too numurous to list.

Collectors are advised to pay a visit to Freemasons' Hall. You will be made very welcome and there is a lot to see that will help you to recognise items that you might like to collect in the future.

Catch the underground to Holborn, leave the station, turn left and head towards BBC House. Great Queen Street is on the right about 300 yards from the station.

MASONIC MEMORABILIA

The Freemasons' emblem of the Square and Compasses are easily recognisable. They are the two working tools of an engineer, a craftsman and a Mason and have become symbolic of Freemasonry the world over. In any language the basic symbol is the same and will be found on so many different items and objects, which makes the job of collecting it a lot easier.

The materials that these Masonic collectables are made of include paper, china, glass, silver, gold and platinum. There are literally thousands and thousands of articles to collect. The benefit to new collectors of limited means is that it enables them to build up a fine collection which will be interesting and may become valuable in future years. Certain items are already very expensive, particularly china, glass and the older jewels. One object of this book is to act as a guide to new collectors, veteran collectors and dealers alike who may be in doubt as to value, whether it be for buying or selling.

Some of the prettiest china and glass is embellished with Masonic designs, and there are many wealthy collectors who collect Masonic artefacts. In France regular auctions take place of Masonic collectables, where impressive illustrated coloured catalogues are produced. There is no shortage of expensive pieces available but this book concentrates on a mixture of items, available at auctions and antique fairs, from the very expensive to the cheaper end of the market.

The speed at which interesting pieces come onto the market is more of a trickle than a flow. Many times have I been into antiques shops with the very open question:

"Have you anything Masonic?" to be told,

"We had a piece some time back, but its gone," or

"No, I haven't seen a piece for ages. I always buy it in when I can".

However, a steady supply of modern Masonic collectables is being produced all the time and they are the antiques of tomorrow.

For the stamp collectors among you, there is a wide range representing Freemasonry from various countries througout the world, of which a few examples are shown opposite, but because of the wide variety I would suggest that it would be more helpful

3 pence Great Britain.   *Set of 4 Jamaican*   *Set of 4 stamps showing the*
                           Commemoratives.   *square & compass.*

to the readers to research this subject through a philately book or magazine. Stanley Gibbons of London has a range of books on the subject which are sold through many bookshops and stationers.

The easiest Masonic collectables to find are the jewels. These are medallions made for Freemasons to wear and have been in use since the middle of the 18th century. They are brightly coloured ribbons with a securing pin and a pretty enamelled medal hanging at the end. They do make an attractive display.

Before 1940, the jewels were made of silver and gold, but today they mainly come in non-precious metals. There are hundreds of different ones to collect, starting at just a few pounds.

If you are a new collector, you will have to decide on how you are going to display your collection; jewels look nice in a display case or framed as shown in this book, and you will find that as your collection grows, the fascination of admiring the designs and history of it will give you immense satisfaction.

Always buy the best you can afford and try to buy from good, established, recognised dealers. Although, it goes without saying, you cannot turn down a good buy at a boot fair or flea market if the opportunity arises. It is advisable to get a detailed receipt listing the item, its approximate date, condition and price. Keep these receipts in a secure place or keep a computer record with digital photographs - this is very helpful.

It is often the way with new collectors to buy everything cheap that they come across so as to accumulate a good number of pieces. Then gradually they will specialise and sell off the less important pieces and improve the quality of their collection. This is the best way to learn the good from the mediocre.

Should you find a rare piece of pottery that has been repaired and you are happy with the price, then buy it. You can always trade it in if a perfect example comes along at a later date. Even the V&A museum have shelves of broken pottery and china, because they cannot find better examples.

SOME MASONIC ORDERS IN FREEMASONRY

There are numerous Masonic orders within the framework of Freemasonry to which a Master Mason may join in addition to his craft lodge.

The Holy Royal Arch

The most well-known order is The Holy Royal Arch. It seems to be as old as Freemasonry itself, although the exact dates of its beginnings are unknown. It evolved over a period of time and has become a voluntarily, but highly recommended furthering of Masonic knowledge for Master Masons. Indeed it has been stated by many that no Mason's education is complete until he has joined The Royal Arch.

The regalia worn by the Holy Royal Arch is an apron, a sash and a jewel. The jewel is a double triangle, in the centre of which is the 'All Seeing Eye'. It is made of gold, silver, or a plated combination and attached to a white ribbon. These jewels are plentiful and can be found in various antique shops and fairs, and make a good starting point for a new collection. The older and larger patterns of this jewel, usually made of silver, are more sought after and will probably fetch between £20-35 ($30-52).

Mark Masonry

This again is an ancient Masonic extension, eventually popularised into modern Masonry. Many brothers have found a happy and fulfilling extension

The Holy Royal Arch Jewel.
Estimate: Non-silver £10-12
($15-18) Silver £12-15 ($18-22)

The Mark Masonry Jewel.
Estimate: Non-silver £10-15
($15-22) Silver £15-20 ($22-30)

to their craft lodges by joining Mark. Its earliest record in English Freemasonry was in 1769. This Masonic brotherhood of Mark Masons have their own rituals and regalia.

The Royal Ark Mariners

This fraternity has had a struggle to survive, but is today established in Freemasonry with Lodges throughout the world. The number 1 Lodge of Royal Ark Mariners was established in 1872. It is becoming more and more popular. The diversification away from the everyday ritual of the craft lodges helps to bring variety into the keen Freemason's life. The regalia is again an apron but the jewel is very unusual. One could quite easily pass it, not realising its Masonic link. The jewel is a semi-circle suspended from a ribbon of many colours, just like the colours of the rainbow. Suspended from the underside of the semi-circle is a dove bearing an olive branch.

The Royal Ark Mariner's Jewel.

Estimate: £10-20 ($15-30)

The Order of Secret Monitor Jewel.

Estimate: £10-20 ($15-30)

The Order of the Secret Monitor

This order is thought to be American in origin. Its regalia is again a sash but the jewel is very smart with two triangles intertwined to form a star and two arrows passing through it. This is suspended from an orange and mauve ribbon.

The Royal and Select Masters

The regalia in this order is very different and colourful. The jewel is a triangle with a crown at the top attached to the ribbon bar. These are not common, and do not conform to what one expects a Masonic jewel to look like.

The Royal and Select Master's jewel.

Estimate: £10-20 ($15-30)

Order of the Allied Masonic Degrees

This was designed to allow all the small but respectable associated fraternities within Freemasonry to be given recognition as a group. Most of them have their own ceremonies, regalia and jewels. These are very colourful and attractive and once again could easily be overlooked by someone not acquainted with them. These jewels also appear on a bar as a set of miniatures.

The Order of the Allied Masonic Degrees' Jewel. Estimate: £15-18 ($22-27)

The Red Cross of Constantine Jewel. Estimate: £20-25 ($30-37)

The Red Cross of Constantine

This order, although not as popular as some others, has a beautiful assortment of regalia and jewels. They bear no resemblance to the standard logo one associates with Freemasonry. But they are branches to which a Mason may belong in addition to his craft lodges.

The jewels belonging to this order are a mixture of crosses, eagles and crowns, with white or red ribbons, and part of the regalia are swords and attractive sashes.

Knights Templars and Knights of Malta

This is possibly the most important of all the brotherhoods associated with Freemasonry. Although it does not style itself exactly on the old Knights Templars, there is no mistaking the similarity in dress. The regalia consists of a cloak, sword, sash, mantle, cap and jewels.

Knights Templars Past Perceptors Collar Jewel (left). Breast Jewel (right). Estimate: £35-65 ($52-97) each.

THE JEWELS OF FREEMASONRY

The word jewel conjures up in the mind of the un-enlightened, an item of great value. In Masonic terms, it refers to a medallion-type of embellishment, worn by brothers to show their position in the progressive ladder of Freemasonry, or as a token of respect. A jewel consists of a clasp or pin with a plate attached which is inscribed with the name of the jewel. Suspended from this bar by an attractive piece of ribbon, is a brightly coloured enamelled medallion, depicting various Masonic emblems and designs. This is the basic format and I would suggest, when ferreting around in a box of odds and ends in a fleamarket or auction, to be alert for any unusual medallions, which might relate to a branch of Freemasonry. This is where the real bargains can be found. Any medallion which has a square, compasses, a triangle, a star, or any other interesting embellishment which does not relate to a particular sport, hobby or association, might be the ancient jewel that everyone else is looking for. Some of the older jewels are very hard to recognise. As your knowledge improves, so the chances of capitalising on that knowledge will bring its rewards.

Some jewels were not issued in medal form, but as brooches, usually made of silver. Like most jewels made since 1900, they will have the year of issue. There are hundreds of different types of jewels available, some very scarce and expensive. It is up to you, the collector, to decide which to collect and what theme to follow.

Stewards' Jewels

There are already two excellent books on the market dealing with this subject in great detail, named in 'Suggested Reading' at the end of this book. However, I feel I am at liberty to at least enlighten the new collector with a few basic facts.

There were until recently two schools founded by the Freemasons for orphaned boys and girls of Freemasons. Every year a festival was held by each of them within the Masonic network, to raise money to help finance the school for the coming year. As a receipt for monies received, a jewel was issued. These were known as Stewards' Jewels, and a brother purchasing it would become a Steward of that particular school for that year. These are the most common jewels that can be collected. They date back to about 1860 until 1985, when the boys' school was disbanded and joined with the Royal Masonic Institute for Girls. Mainly from 1900 to 1940 these jewels were made of silver, and after that base metal was used. During the war, when material was scarce, jewels were made of cardboard and plastic. At the request of The Grand Lodge, many jewels were voluntarily handed in to be melted down to help in the war effort. This sacrifice, although a very noble and generous act, removed thousands of valuable jewels from the reach of collectors. But nevertheless there are still many that can be found today. These jewels are easily recognisable, with a nameplate at the top reading 'STEWARD'.

The colour of the ribbon will signify whether it is for the boys' or girls' school, i.e.:

White: Royal Masonic Institute for Girls (RMIG) Founded 1788

Blue: Royal Masonic Institute for Boys (RMIB) Founded 1798

Red: Royal Masonic Benevolent Institute (RMBI) Founded 1842

Sometimes a brooch was issued instead of a jewel in a particular year. One should expect to pay a lot less for a non-silver jewel made after 1940. Jewels made before that date will rise in price accordingly, depending on age, condition and scarcity. You can buy a standard bi-metal Steward's Jewel for a couple of pounds. However, I have seen similar in some antiques shops for twenty times that amount. I think those shops will have them for a very long time. Many hundreds of each of these Stewards' Jewels exist and all relevant information regarding quantity, county and design for each year is recorded in *Stewards' Jewels*.

HALLMARKS and ASSAY OFFICE

The London Goldsmiths received a Royal Charter forming them into the Worshipful Company of Goldsmiths on 30th March, 1327. It gave them the powers to enforce the assay and hallmarking laws. The word 'Hallmark' comes from Goldsmiths Hall, the headquarters of the company.

The hallmark is applied to precious metal after a test by an official Assay Office, to denote fineness of quality. There are two qualities of silver, 92.5 Sterling silver and 95.8 Britannia silver. Gold has four qualities at the present time, 916 - 22 carat, 750 -18 carat, 585 - 14 carat and 375 - 9 carat.

There are many inexpensive books on hallmarks that are available which will explain the grades and marks of the Assay offices.

However, when buying gold, silver or platinum always look for the hallmarks, especially the main ones. Generally, British gold should always have the grade of the gold (ie. 750 or 18). Sterling silver generally carries the Lion Passant (passing) or the 925 grade.

Sometimes, gold is gilded onto silver which can be confusing for the buyer who sees a hallmark and thinks he is buying gold. Remember, no matter what the surface might be, silver has a lion passant and gold should have the grade.

Also, there is a lot of gold coming into the UK which is marked as 18 carat or 750, but is in fact plated gold with a core of brass. The only way this can be tested is to scrape the surface layer and apply Nitric Acid. If the core is brass, greenish dark bubbles will appear. (Nitric acid should be used with great care as it can cause dangerous burns to the skin). If in doubt, don't buy.

Marks generally found on Silver:-

London		
Birmingham		
Sheffield		

Gold will also carry: 22ct. or 916, 18ct or 750, 14ct or 585, 9ct or 375.

There are other Assay offices of which Edinburgh and Dublin still exist, and some which have now closed. All these marks can be found in various publications on silver assay marks.

Standard Silver Mark

Masonic Charity Jewel.

Silver jewels are of course much scarcer and more expensive. A fair price would be between £8 and £20, rising upwards, again depending on scarcity and condition. Unless they pre-date 1900, the price should never exceed £20. When buying jewels, do make sure that they are in good condition, with the enamel intact and complete with pin. Also check that the ribbons are not tatty, unless of course you know the jewels to be rare, which very few are. Many jewels before 1940 came in jewel boxes. These attractive little cases are collectable in their own right - some of them date back to Victorian times and were made by firms that have now gone out of production.

They can be bought for as little as £1 each. Sometimes jewel collectors are quite happy to part with them, because they prefer to display their jewels in display cases and have no need for boxes.

The early jewels issued in Freemasonry were not enamelled and some were made of precious metals, but take care when buying, particularly from the Internet. The assay marks can be confusing and easily misunderstood. A colleague of mine tried to purchase a Royal Arch jewel advertised on the Web. The buyer stated it was 22K when in fact it was gold-plated over a silver hallmark. The seller insisted it had been tested as gold. It is difficult to verify pieces when you are dealing with items seen only on the Web. Finding you have been duped after you have purchased is not a nice experience and not always easy to rectify. Many Masonic pieces including jewels can be bought on the Web, but do be careful. Another true case of mistaken identity concerns a jewel which not only looks to be gold but is clearly hallmarked 14karat gold on the rim, when in fact only the rim frame of the jewel is actually gold. The jewel itself, which appears to be gold, is a base metal, gilded to give this effect - not to deceive, just to blend in with the frame that holds it. I saw this particular jewel on an antique stall in Somerset and realising what it was, but not being able to see it clearly in the showcase, I asked if I might take it out. Sure enough it was the same jewel, so out of curiosity I looked at the price. I saw it was £300. When I exploded at seeing the price, the stallholder (who I'm sure in all innocence) pointed out it was all gold and insisted on it, despite what I told him. It was only when I explained that he was not the first to be misled into thinking that the jewel was all gold, that he reluctantly agreed that perhaps I knew more than he did about it. It is very important when dealing with these older jewels to clearly establish whether they are gold or silver. The marks look very similar, especially if it is plated gold on silver.

Moose and The Oddfellows are four of the better known and still practicing Friendly Societies; and I use that word loosely for want of a better one, as there are many more societies like these, very honourable, some with a very long history, whose names I am not familiar with. Indeed, most of them have secret signs and passwords of their own which are secret to them alone. But they are not classed as secret societies.

Out of them all, 'The Buffs' are perhaps the most well-known. They have a history dating back over 200 years and the buffalo head is their emblem. It can be clearly seen on their jewels and regalia. The Buffs, like the Freemasons, tend to produce more jewels of splendid colour and design than any other society; and in large quantities too. It is also common practice for many dealers (who know no better) to use a collective word of 'Masonic' for all jewels, in the hope that the word alone will entice the unenlightened collector to purchase or bid for them.

The Moose, another well-known and very popular society practising throughout the UK, has a moose's head as its emblem, always depicted in profile, never face on. It is worth noting these points as it can save you a lot of money and time if you know what you are purchasing. If you are not sure, ask questions about what you are buying. Sometimes you will have to go by your own gut feeling that a particular jewel or other memento is related to Freemasonry, because there are some excellent pieces to be found that have still not been categorised and are virtually unresearched in terms of origin and value.

SELECTION OF COLLECTABLE
MASONIC JEWELS

A selection of Stewards' jewels issued in the World War 11 period and just after when raw materials were scarce. These are made of cardboard, plastic, a pewter-type metal and fabric. It is interesting to note that on the reverse of the 1943 jewel there was a pledge to replace the cardboard jewel with a proper metal jewel after the war. The Steward jewel for R.M.I.B. states on the reverse that this cardboard token jewel is a form of receipt for two shillings and sixpence (13p of the metal value of the jewel) for the relief of distress occasioned by the war.

These war-time jewels are very much sought after, and can usually be found at small fairs and markets. Estimate: £12-15 each ($18-22)

A trio of Masonic Benevolent Institute Jewels.

Stewards' Jewels R.M.I.B.

Stewards' Jewels R.M.I.G.

This picture shows a Mark Jewel, and two Stewards' Jewels.

Different and very attractive R.M.I.G. Jewels in base metal. There are a lot of these available to collect.

These jewels are of the same commercial value as those with ribbons. Some of the Stewards' Jewels were issued with ribbons and some without, as shown here.

All the above jewels are very common and would have an estimated value of £4-8 ($6-12), according to condition. Silver examples would be more, £12-20 according to age and condition.

Different R.M.I.B. Jewels. These are very plentiful and are base metal.
Estimate: £4-8 ($6-12)

Middle Jewel is a QC Lodge Correspondence Circle Members Jewel.
Estimate: £15-20 ($22.50-30).
The Jewels L & R are Stewards' Jewels, which have additional metal attachments on the ribbons. A small increase on the value of the basic Stewards' Jewels would be expected. In some years fewer jewels were issued, resulting in higher prices. All the relevant information regarding individual jewels and the numbers that were issued can be found in 'Further Reading' at the end of this book.
Estimate: £5-15 ($7-22), according to condition and age.

A serious collector would not buy these Jewels - devoid of ribbons and clasps. Even in silver, they are only worth around £2 each ($3)

From left to right - A Steward's Jewel, a jewel commemorating 150 years of Grand Lodge and a special Steward's Jewel which is not gold. Estimate: Left: £5 ($7.50).
Mid: £12 ($18). Right: £25 ($40)

A pair of Provincial-type Officer Collar Jewels. The Somerset one (right) is made of silver and would be the more expensive of the two.
Estimate: (London) £10-15 ($15-22).
(Somerset) £25-35 ($37-50).

A Past Master's Collar Jewel. Solid silver.
Estimate: £50-60 ($75-90) in this form.

Two very fine Founders' Jewels, silver with
painted enamel pictures on each jewel.
Estimate: £40-50 ($60-75)

Two views of a Masonic Charity Jewel
which sometimes has a 14 carat rim, with a
basic metal jewel. Estimate: £40-45 ($60-
67). With silver gilt £30-35 ($45-50)

Grand Steward's Lodge
special design Centenary Jewel. Set with
Brilliants. This Jewel is known as the Hogarth
Pattern and is most scarce in original form.
Estimate: £300-350 ($450-525)

A most unusual 15 karat gold presentation jewel, 1890, with safety chain. It is inscribed on the back. It has a blue centre boss with the letter 'J' on it. Presented to the Master of a lodge for his outstanding services. Estimate: £140-175 ($210-262)

Knight Templar Past Perceptors.
Left: Collar jewel. Silver.
Right: Breast Jewel. Silver.
Estimate: £35-65 ($52-97) each.

Lodge Chaplain's silver jewel of unusual Georgian design.
Estimate: £60-100 ($90-150)

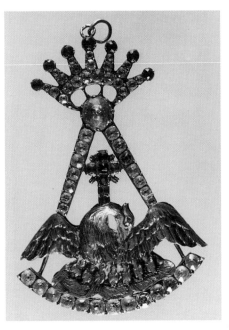

Rose Croix Jewel in French paste.
Estimate: £100-175 ($150-262)

Knights Grand Cross.
Estimate: £125-150 ($187-225)

Special Centenary Jewel for
Newstead Lodge, Nottingham
in original pattern.
Estimate: £60-70 ($90-110)

R.M.I.B. Acting Vice-President Festival
Jewel (silver).
Estimate: £60-100 ($90-150)

39

A framed set of mixed Benevolent and Stewards' Jewels of Somerset. Estimate: £100-110 ($150-165)

Miniature jewels for watch chain. Estimated: £35-50 ($52-75) Provincial Grand Master Festival Jewel dated 1869 (silver). Estimate: £40-60 ($60-90)

Engraved plate jewel. Estimate: £350-400 ($525-600)

GLE 1887 Victorian Jubilee jewel.
Estimate: £100-150 ($150-225)

The first Freemasons Hall jewel.
Estimate: £600-700 ($900-1,050)

Provincial collar jewel c.1830 Made by
Ackland.
Estimate: £95-115 ($142-172)

Hogarth pattern. Grand Steward Lodge Jewel
1777 Original design.
Estimate: £500-600 ($750-900)

Pierced Lodge jewel
Estimate: £350-450 ($525-675)

Grand Lodge Mark Master Mason
Jewel.
Estimate: £10-12 ($15-18)

Past Master Chapter jewel.
Estimate: £95-110 ($142-165)

Third generation Royal Arch jewel depicting the arch and pavement.
Estimate: £300-400 ($450-600)

Hallmarked pierced jewel c.1810
Estimate: £300-400 ($450-600)

Secretary jewel Kilwenney Lodge, near Edinburgh, 1769.
Estimate: £300-350 ($450-525)

Wiltshire Grand Secretary Jewel, showing Georgian Hallmark. Estimate: £250-300 ($375-400)

Whitehaven Masons Rifle Club 1859.
Estimate: £100-125 ($150-187)

Past Masters' Jewel.
Estimate: £60-80 ($90-120)

Possibly French Prisoner-of-War
Jewel. Estimate: £200-300
($300-450)

Old Tauntonman Chapter
Jewel. Estimate: £60-80
($90-120)

1790 Royal Arch Jewel of
unusual design.
Estimate: £350-400
($252-600)

Treasurer's jewel after
Thomas Harper style.
Estimate: £200-250
($300-375)

Ancient pattern breast jewel by
T. Harper. Estimate: £300-400
($450-600)

1790s Pre-union Past Masters' jewel.
Estimate: £350-400 ($252-600)

Irish paste jewel.
Estimate: £100-150 ($150-225)

1790 Engraved plate jewel. Met in Frome. Old Somerset Lodge. Now extinct.
Estimate: £300-400 ($450-600)

CENTENARY JEWELS

The following are a selection of special designed centenary jewels issued pre 1867. Less than 50 designs were granted permission prior to 1867. Since then only the regulation pattern can be used as shown on the left. However, special dispensation was granted to a few lodges since that date.

These early centenary jewels are very collectable and can fetch between £70-90 ($105-135) According to condition.

Left: Regulation Centenary jewel used after 1867 up to the present day. (See page 30)

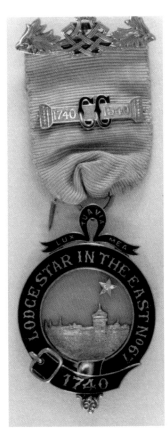

Cloth Regalia Worn in Lodge

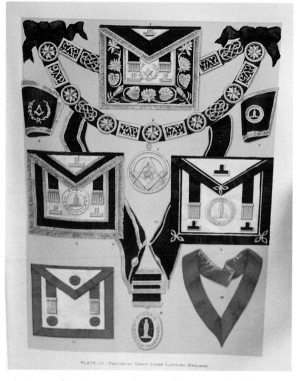

A picture showing a complete set of Provincial Lodge regalia.

Cloth regalia worn in lodge comes in a huge variety of designs and colours and there is so much to collect. A full set comprising apron, collars and cuffs can be found for about £40. You can find regalia in markets and small antique shops all over the world. Much of the more senior grades in Freemasonry have aprons and collars covered in attractive gold wire braiding. The more senior the officer, the more embellished is his apron and collar. The finest example is that worn by the current Duke of Kent, who is The Grand Master of England.

If you go to The Grand Lodge Museum and Library at Great Queen Street in London, you will see regalia and jewels, together with the largest, most impressive collection of china, glass and other artefacts.

Aprons are worn by Freemasons in their lodges, and are often made of fine leather. They have been worn by practicing Stonemasons for more than a thousand years; a short apron around the waist shows the rank of the brother in the lodge. They become more colourful and braided as he rises to higher levels. They are the brother's personal regalia, so do not belong to the lodge.

Knight Templar Apron. Estimate: £40-80 ($60-120) Depending on condition.

Some of these are manufactured and painted by individual brothers to their own interpretation, design and colour. In the mid-19th century, the pattern on all regalia was standardised, but early aprons can still be found, though in general they are very frail. When collecting regalia, the most common craft degree to be found in abundance is that belonging to the Master Masons in Craft Lodges. It is unmistakable with a white background and light-blue fittings. The apron of a Master Mason has two light blue rosettes, one in each corner of the lower half and one rosette in the centre of the triangular flap pointing downwards.

When a brother has served his time in the chair of King Solomon, he wears a different apron, one with taus or bright metal upturned Ts. This singles him out from his junior brethren. There are also three pairs of cuffs, each with their own emblem. Page 50 shows a selection of Masonic craft regalia for the collector. Scotland and Ireland have their own colours as do many other crafts of Freemasonry outside of the UK.

Regalia is not the easiest of items to store, but makes a fine display. Regalia is best hung from a clip-type coathanger. Buy an old wardrobe and make space for it in your house or garage, to create the ideal storage solution.

In Britain there are nearly 100 shops selling Masonic regalia. They not only sell new but also secondhand pieces and sometimes offer part exchange. These shops are also ideal for buying secondhand jewels as most of them have a good selection at reasonable

Rear of Rose Croix Collar Sash
Estimate: £30-50 ($45-75)

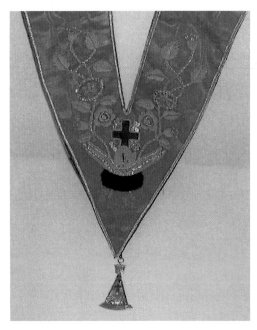

Front of Rose Croix Collar
Estimate: £40-60 ($60-90)

prices - and the shop owner will always help and advise you.

This is also true of some of the museums. Remember, they have to raise money to pay for the upkeep of the museum. Very often they have duplicate jewels and regalia to sell. You will get the best advice there and I am sure you will find some fine examples of jewels and regalia for purchase.

In the past I have exchanged pieces with museums. Museums are always looking for new exhibits and will pay a fair price for any that they really want.

If you have pieces you want to buy, sell or exchange, advertise in local papers, and antique magazines etc.

POTTERY AND PORCELAIN

Rare Wedgwood Creamware mug with a good selection of black printed Masonic symbols and a verse from The Entered Apprentice song which is still used in lodge festive boards today. 6" high.
Estimate: £600-900 ($900-1,350)

It is a fact that good examples of Masonic pottery and porcelain are expensive, but there are collectors who are prepared to invest in it. The majority of items collected in this field were made from the late 18th to the late 19th century and are particularly associated with factories in Liverpool, Staffordshire, Newcastle and Sunderland, who were prolific producers of Masonic china.

Wedgwood was one of the first factories to produce Masonic china. In the mid-18th century, potteries tried to emulate hard-paste porcelain introduced and used by the Chinese for many hundreds of years. During experiments at Wedgwood, an error occurred in the production and from this they discovered a very smooth cream-coloured china, which they found was ideal for painting and printing on. They named it 'Creamware' and it proved so popular that by the end of that century most factories were producing their own form of creamware.

It was produced throughout the 19th century. Early pieces of Masonic creamware, in good condition, are hard to find but do occasionally crop up at antique fairs. Be prepared to pay high three figure sums upwards, for an early 18th century piece. It is worth remembering that these jugs and mugs were meant to be used and were not intended as showroom pieces, so most of them are chipped or broken.

Lustreware - Reproduction & Faked Ware

Because Sunderland Lustreware has become so collectable and much of it is unmarked, there are many fakes and reproductions on the market.

A.E. Gray & Co. Ltd., Stoke-on-Trent, produced reproduction pink/purple lustreware of the Wear Bridge and seafaring designs in and around 1950s-60s; they were made to look like early 19th century Sunderland Lustreware. They did, however, carry a 1950s-60s backstamp of a sailing ship with 'Gray's Pottery, made in Stoke-On-Trent', but sometimes forgers have removed this and sold pieces on as original 19th century. So be careful when buying Sunderland Lustreware - always study where the backstamp should be for any signs of tampering.

More difficult to spot are the reproductions intended to deceive. Some of these fakes originated in the 1930s, others in Staffordshire around the 1960s. The heavier lustre is more easily distinguished from the earlier Sunderland ware, and mugs and jugs do not have the usual tell-tale rings where they have been thrown on a wheel by hand.

Mark of Gray's Pottery, Hanley, England

Many pieces depict verses of Masonic songs. A Wedgwood Creamware jug, dated 1780, has the following verse, taken from the Entered Apprentice song:

The world is in pain their secrets to gain
But still let them wonder and gaze on
For they nere can devine the word nor the sign
Of a free and an accepted Mason.

This same verse also appears on some lustreware, over 100 years later.

Sunderland Lustreware originated in the Sunderland area or North-East England and has become a generic term for a technique used to decorate pottery involving metal dissolved in acid, which is then painted on and fired. The metals originally employed were silver, gold, copper and platinum. Only platinum yields a silver colour. Silver produces a straw colour, gold a ruby-red and copper a colour which ranges from yellowish-red to a deep coppery-red. Some of the best lustre pottery on which copper was used is found among the early 14th century Hispano-Moresque specimens. Gold (red) and copper-lustre, regarded as poor quality in comparison, occurs on the early 19th century pottery of what we know as Sunderland ware. The colour most popular for collectors seems to be pink and can be found at most antique fairs, but even so, what is rare and very collectable is the Sunderland ware with Masonic logos. Jugs were the most popular item, but there were so many different items of Masonic ware produced this way that one could assemble a whole dinner service out of them. There are still plates, bowls and butter dishes to be found, although time has taken its toll and pieces are getting fewer. Nearly all lustreware is unsigned, but

Lustre Jug

one can often find a signed print or transfer within the design.

There were scores of potteries in the North of England, Scotland and Wales, all producing at some time their own style of lustreware, but the name is synonymous with Sunderland. How one tells the difference between manufacturers comes only with experience and sometimes a bit of luck.

Transfer prints were used in the decorating of these household items; this was a quick and easy method of adornment. Many Sunderland jugs used transfers depicting the Iron Bridge on one side and Masonic symbols, in colour, on the other. There were so many pots and jugs produced that the assembly lines didn't take care of quality. There was little or no care taken in some factories. However, it is worth pointing out that a normal Sunderland Lustre jug can fetch between £500-700 ($600-900) at auction. If it carries Masonic symbols its value can be even more.

Not all transfer ware was pink. You can find some highlighted with yellow, green and other pastel shades. Many pieces of Sunderland Lustreware were specially commissioned for Masonic couples about to marry. These can be very attractive with Masonic verses on one side and flowers on the other with the front painted with the name of the bride and groom and the date of their marriage in elegant copperplate script. Sometimes they were designed for anniversaries. Generally Sunderland Lustreware is unmarked, but some designers did print their names on the transfers. These rare pieces are even more collectable. Many of these wares were exported to Holland and Scandinavia. Some were specially commissioned with a customer's particular poem or transfer dedicated to a loved one.

If you are fortunate you may find jugs with a Masonic logo on one side and a Crimean War design on the other. The jugs were most popular during the Victorian period while the potteries were also very busy producing thousands of pieces of the Queen's commemorative ware. However, Freemasonry is universal; you are just as likely to have a better chance to find a Sunderland Masonic Lustreware jug in Bombay or

Antwerp than perhaps you would in the UK. There are individual potteries that can be associated with lustreware; such as Dixon & Co, Moore and Co, Southwick Sunderland, J. Phillips and Co. or the Sunderland or Garrison Pottery. Scotland is prolific with Masonic collectables. It is believed Freemasonry started there, developed from the Knights Templars. Scotland can certainly trace its Masonic heritage back hundreds of years and it is far more respected there than in England.

A dealer friend of mine finds most of his stock in Scotland and travels the Isles for it. Prices are rising even while I am writing this book. Pieces I bought last year for £500 are now worth £700 or more. This year I was offered a Newcastle Lustreware jug in showroom condition. On one side were all the Freemason signs, the pillars, and the chequered flooring, on the other was a hand-painted bunch of flowers. This pretty jug, about 10" high, was more than I could afford at £1,700 and I declined the offer. It was sold to a lady for the full asking price. Another similar jug, I looked at and declined because it was cracked, went for £750. Recently on the Web I enquired if an export dealer had any Masonic jugs and a reply came back in minutes saying, "Just the one jug at £1,600."

The drinking pots or mugs, lustreware in particular, like the jugs and other utensils used in the home, were of similar design and by the same potteries. The Garrison Pottery was a very industrious company, though their wares were thought to be a little suspect. The transfers on their mugs and jugs were highlighted with paint in a slapdash manner, but despite this one can still expect to pay £500 plus, depending on condition.

The Wear Bridge in Sunderland, which features on so many lustreware pieces, was originally a curved bridge, but it was rebuilt after 1859, so if you find a picture of it on a piece of pottery depicting a straight bridge, you can be pretty certain it was produced after 1859.

Frog Mugs

Other items worth a mention are the Masonic frog mugs. These were drinking mugs with a china frog stuck on the inside, the idea being that as the unsuspecting drinker neared the end of his drink, he would suddenly see a frog staring at him! So few of the original mugs remain that I suspect many were dropped in fright. These are very collectable. An article published in *Antiques & Collectables* Magazine in 1999 quotes an auction price of around £300 ($450) for one of these mugs. Today, the figure for an undamaged frog mug would be much nearer £500 ($750). However, there are many forgeries on the market, so it does pay to be extra cautious with these mugs.

Masonic frog mug.

A frog mug, height 5". This particular mug is in pristine condition. It was made in 1840 after the amalgamation of the Masonic crafts of 1813, hence the difference in the symbols shown on earlier jugs, many of which are omitted. On one side there are the new Masonic symbols while on the other side there is a beautifully clear print of the bridge over the River Wear. It is inscribed on the transfer: Moore & Southwick (the manufacturers) and this makes it even more collectable and rarer. Estimate: £450-650 ($675-975)

An extremely rare plate measuring 9" across. It was formerly from the Geoffrey Godden collection, and is the only recorded example of a signed print by Thomas Bradley on porcelain. Circa 1810. It shows the crest of the Grand Lodge of England before the amalgamation in 1813.
Estimate: £400-600 ($600-900)

Creamware lustre jug, circa 1830, 10" high, with a grapevine collar painted around the top. On one side is a hand painted illustration over a transfer of Masonic symbols and on the reverse is The Iron Bridge over the River Wear, which was built by R Burdon in1793.
This is a fine example of a creamware jug of this period. Estimate: £650-800 ($975-1,200)

Creamware mug measuring 6" high by 4" wide, circa 1800. A quart capacity mug, transfer printed with bright colour over paint. Unlike most mugs of this period the transfer shows an unusual picture of four ladies. The mug was manufactured in the age of the Ancients of Freemasonry, a period leading up to the eventual amalgamation of the two types of Masonry in 1813, whose form today is modern-style Masonry. The ancients had their own symbols, many of which were not adopted by the newly-formed Masonry in 1813.
Estimate: £400-650 ($600-975)

Modern pottery plate measuring 8" diameter, showing the arms of Marine Lodge 232. This lodge came from Calcutta in 1976 and came out at its bi-centenary. Even though modern it would still rate an estimated price of £20-25 ($60-90)

Marks on Sunderland Lustreware

Amongst the many potteries that produced Sunderland lustreware, only a few produced quality examples and most of these had an impressed mark on the base. These are of interest to collectors because very few are found. Factory names found on transfer prints, usually at the bottom of a verse or saying, are not always reliable. Some marks with their dates are produced here by kind permission of E.George Perrott's Pottery & Porcelain Marks book.

1788-99 Atkinson & Co., Southwick Pottery, Sunderland.

	Impressed or printed	**ATKINSON & CO**

1788-	**Southwick Pottery, Sunderland.**	1788-1829 Anthony Scott & Co.	**A. SCOTT & CO** **SCOTT, SOUTHWICK**
		c.1829-44 A. Scott & Sons	**A. SCOTT & SONS** **S. & SONS**
		c.1844-54 Scott Brothers & Co.	**S.B. & CO.** **SCOTT BROTHERS**
		c.1854-97 A. Scott & Sons	**A. SCOTT & SONS** **S. & S.**
1799-	**John Dawson, Sunderland.**	c.1799-1864 South Hylton & Ford Potteries.	**DAWSON** **I. DAWSON**
		1800-64 Various printed marks incorporating the name	**DAWSON & CO** **LOW FORD** **FORD POTTERY** **J. DAWSON** **SOUTH HYLTON**
		c.1837-48 Thomas Dawson & Co.	**DAWSON & CO.**
1802-	**Union Pottery, Sunderland.**	Printed	**UNION POTTERY**
1803-	**Samuel Moore & Co., Wear Pottery, Sunderland.**		
		1803-74 Various impressed or printed marks which include name or initials	**MOORE & CO** **SUNDERLAND** **S. MOORE & CO.** **S.M. & CO.**

1807-65 Sunderland or 'Garrison' Pottery, Sunderland.

	c.1807-12 J. Phillips. Impressed	**J. PHILLIPS** **SUNDERLAND POTTERY**
	c.1813-19 Phillips & Co. Dixon & Co.	**PHILLIPS & CO** **DIXON &CO.**
	c.1820-26 Dixon, Austin & Co.	**DIXON, AUSTIN & CO.**
	c.1827-40 Dixon, Austin, Phillips & Co.	**DIXON, AUSTIN,** **PHILLIPS & CO**
	Dixon, Austin & Co.	**DIXON, AUSTIN & CO.**
	c.1840-65 Dixon Phillips & Co.	**DIXON PHILLIPS & CO.**

1857	**William Ball, Deptford Pottery, Sunderland.**	**COPYRIGHT BALL**
	Ball purchased copper transfer plates from Garrison, Moore's and Scott's when they closed down. Makers names were rarely erased so Dixon's name can be found on Ball's orange lustreware. When Ball's closed down, these plates were sold on and became the origin of reproduction ware.	**BROS** **SUNDERLAND**

Attractive Sunderland Lustre jug, 6" high, circa 1850-1860, made at the time of the Crimean War. There was a great interest in England for pictures and prints showing scenes from this war. This one shows a poem on one side, which reads:

Let Masonry from pole to pole,
Her sacred laws expand,
Far as the mighty waters roll,
To was remotest land:
That virtue has not left mankind.
Her social maxims prove,
For stamped upon the Masons' mind,
Are unity and love.

Surrounded by a wreath of flowers and intertwined with Masonic symbols, on the reverse is a picture of two soldiers dressed in the period of the Crimean War. One a Frenchman, and the other English shaking hands and each carrying their country's national flag. Above their heads is a yellow scroll on which are the words May they ever unite. Estimate: £400-500 ($600-750)

A beautiful genuine 'Kirk' series Wedgwood plate, 9" diameter, in blue and white, showing Masonic symbols in the tiny circle. Circa 1800.
Estimate: £175-200 ($260-300)

60

A splendid example of a pink lustreware jug, circa 1829 and 10" high. It shows how the potteries of the day paid little attention to the accuracy of what they were portraying on their wares. In many cases an assembly line of workers slapped on transfers and quickly applied paints to meet a target for the day on their production run. Here we see a transfer applied in haste. The transfer comes from a period before the actual manufacture of the jug, which can be misleading. Be that as it may, it is a splendid robust brightly pink mottled jug, on which are two poems; the one on the reverse side reads:

Swiftly see each moment flies,
See and learn be timely wise,
Every moment shortens day,
Every pulse beats life away,
Thus thy every heaving breath,
Waft thee on to certain death,
Seize the moments as they fly,
Know to live and learn to die.

At the front of the jug is another small poem, this shows a sailing ship with a poem below which is surrounded by a black and white floral border.
The poem reads:

Glide on my bark the summers tide,
Is gently flowing by thy side;
Around thy prow the waters bright,
In circling rounds of broken light,
Are glittering as if ocean gave,
Her countless gems to deck the wave.

It is a pretty jug, but even here, the worker in haste, has allowed pink lustre paint to run into the edge of the poem, although fortunately not obliterating it. Estimate: £500-700 ($750-1,050)

A fine Sunderland Lustre bowl 5" high and 11" across, painted inside and out with Masonic scenes, poems and the sailor's farewell. It also has a large transfer painting of the Crimean War. Enriched with colour, on the bottom of the bowl is a poem:

> The sailor testing stormy seas,
> Though far his bark may roam,
> Still hears a voice in every breeze,
> that wakens thoughts of home;
> He thinks upon his distant friends,
> His wife, his humble cot,
> And from his inmost heart ascends,
> The prayer-Forget me not.

Inside the bowl is a wife and child in tears as the sailor father pulls himself away to go to sea, his ship is in the bay and there is a poem:

> Sweet. Oh sweet is that sensation,
> Where two hearts in union meet,
> But the pain of separation,
> Mingles bitter with the sweet.

A fine bowl circa 1850-60. Estimate: £350-600 ($525-900)

Unusual copper lustre jug 7" high with Masonic logo of square and compasses on its base.
Estimate: £200-250 ($300-375)

This is another very good example of a Sunderland pink lustre bowl, 10" across and 4" high, circa 1840 and made by Dixon & Co., Sunderland. Again it commemorates a sailor's farewell with Masonic implications in the symbols. Inside the bowl is a poem:

Women make men love,

Love makes them sad

Sadness makes them drink,

and drinking sets them mad.

There is a further poem on this bowl:

Remember me when this you see,

And keep you in my mind,

For let the world say what they will,

Speak of me as you find.

Estimate: £450-650 ($625-975)

20th century drinking mug, 10" tall, in Creamware made by Grays Pottery, Stoke-on-Trent. There is a beautifully illustrated Masonic emblem on one side and on the other is a poem:

Hail MASONRY devine!

Glory of ages shine,

Long may'st thou reign!

Where'er thy LODGES stand,

May they have great command,

And always grace the land,

Thou ART divine!

(This is exactly how it is written). It is obviously a copy of an older mug, as the words 'Made in England' appear on the base. There are several others in this series. Estimate: £50-70 ($75-105)

Large pottery Pearlware Sunderland pink lustre Masonic jug, 10" high, circa 1840, with transfer prints of The Gardener's Arms, and inset is a picture of Adam & Eve in the Garden of Eden. On the front is a transfer print of The Mariners Compass while on the opposite side is a poem of Masonic verse surrounded by a garland of flowers and portraying Masonic symbols.
Estimate: £650-950 ($975-1,425)

Magnificent blue and white mug, with a floral border around the top, outside and inside, 5" high and 3.5" wide. The handle is decorated with fencing and shrubs, on one side is a blue transfer print of two sailors holding flags, with a cannon and cannon balls, and ships in the background, a shield with Mariners Arms and anchor. A scroll below the shield reads 'Deus Davit Vela'. On the opposite side is a conglomeration of various Masonic emblems, and the mug is inscribed "R&E Young, 1826". It is illustrated and referred to in a book called Blue and White China by A. W. Coysh & Hemmingwood. This fine specimen is estimated at £500-800 ($750-1,200)

Large blue meat charger, 1820, maker unknown. This is part of a dinner service, made especially for the Royal Masonic Institute for Girls. No exact figures are available as to the number of settings, but it is thought that with the number of residents at that time it would be 50. The picture on the plate shows the first building on Great Queen Street, which was purchased by The Grand Lodge. The front part facing onto the road was The Freemasons Tavern. Entrance to the Masonic rooms at the rear was through a side door of the building. This large hall was used as a dining room. The picture shows a crocodile of girls leaving the hall with their Governor. This large plate is very rare being the sole survivor of just two known of that size. The plate was made in two smaller sizes, which occasionally appear at auction, as does the odd soup or dinner plate. A soup plate from the service is in the museum at Great Queen Street. The size of this meat charger is 21" x 14". This type of transfer pottery was called View Ware and was mostly produced for the American market. The buildings to the right of the tavern on the plate are still standing today. The value at auction for the large meat charger would be around £2,000 ($3000) and you could expect to pay £350 ($525) for a soup dish at auction. There is a picture of this meat charger in a book by Gillian Neale called Blue & White Pottery.

Dinner plate with view of Grand Lodge Estimate: £250-£350 ($375-525)

These pictures of creamware jugs have been kindly donated by the Poole Masonic Museum together with many other artefacts in this book. It is difficult to be accurate when assessing the values of these types of jugs. It is estimated that this type of 18th century creamware jug with transfer prints can fetch anything between £1,000-1,500 ($1,500-2,250). However, if you find them with a Masonic logo, the price could be £250-500 ($375-750) more. They are extremely rare items and even in a distressed condition, with chips and showing wear, they are still very collectable. Jugs of this rarity are seldom seen outside museums and in some cases could be worth a lot more than my estimates.

Masonic Goss crested ware with typical Freemasonry emblems. Estimate: £60-150 ($90-225), depending on size and quality.

Very rare Meissen enamelled gold-rimmed triangular Snuff Box, with masonic symbols. This box was valued recently for insurance purposes at £18,000 ($27,000)

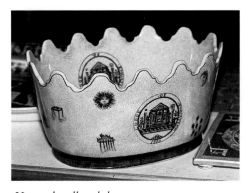

Unusual scalloped shape pottery bowl with Masonic symbols. Estimate: £1,200-1,500 ($1,800-2,250)

Red transfer creamware jug c.1790 with Masonic entered apprentice song on the other side. Estimate: £350-500

Royal Doulton Blue and white centenary jug. Dated 1906. Estimate: £300-400

SUNDERLAND LUSTREWARE BUTTER DISH

A butter dish complete with lid, 4" high, circa 1850. Much pink lustreware in complete dinner services was produced in this style in the mid-19th century. Today, if you searched very hard you might be lucky to find a few serving dishes and plates like this. Many potteries were producing it, and many didn't mark their work. This butter dish has clear Masonic signs on one side and a poem on the other, which reads as follows:

I envy no one 'is birth or fame,
Their title, train, or dress,
Nor has my pride e'er stretched its aim
Beyond what I possess,
I ask not, wish not, to appear
More beauteous, rich or gay,
Lord make me wiser every year,
And better every day

Estimate: £400-600 ($600-900)

A very unusual Masonic Staffordshire figure of a man dressed in an apron and holding a book. Circa 1810. Bought by myself for £400 ($600). None of my Masonic collector friends have seen such a Staffordshire figure like this before, and as such it could be that much more valuable.

An early creamware mug, 6" high by 3" across, possibly Wedgwood, with the ancients Masonic print, circa 1780. Estimate: Mint Condition £450-700 ($675-1,050)

A fine example of creamware pottery, 6" high by 3" across, circa 1820.
In immaculate condition, with print marks for J. Phillips & Co., Sunderland (Garrison Pottery). It was not unusual at this time for pottery to be sold to another factory in a undecorated state for them to decorate.
It is worth remembering that these pieces were made to be used - it is not unusual to find many of them with minor foot rim chips. Estimate: £350-600 ($525-900)

Masonic Oval plate.
Estimate: £70-100 ($105-150)

Masonic Early 8" plate c.1820, Hand-painted. Estimate: £200-250 ($300-375)

Assortment of mixed engraved glasses from Poole Museum.

GLASS

This material lends itself so beautifully to emphasise the art of engraving and etching. There are absolutely delightful examples where the patient skill of the engraver has produced exquisite designs incorporating the Masonic logo. The better ones will be found at antique markets and auctions. You are unlikely to find these at fleamarkets or boot fairs. They are sought-after by collectors and you will be lucky to find a good example under £500. Beware of the difference between engraved and etched glass. Before the advent of electricity, glass engraving was done either by hand or with the use of a carborundum, abrasive wheel. It was a skill that had to be learnt over the years and it took craftsmen to achieve the fine designs of that early period. Today, electronically etched glass does not have the same appearance; it doesn't have the depth of the early pieces because the older glass was much thicker.. In contrast, if you study an original and modern piece together, you can see that the earlier piece has a quite distinctive grey finish.

Finding a skilled glass engraver in England was very difficult in the early 19th century. There were some quite skilled amateurs but nobody could equal the brilliance of the Bohemian glass engravers. Their skill was unsurpassed and it was a skill often kept within a family - passed from father to son. Eventually one or two Bohemian engravers

Bohemian red wine glass, 5" high, heavily embossed with
Masonic emblems. Circa 1900.
Estimate: £200-250 ($300-375)

were enticed to come to England to practice. Very soon their work was in great demand in England. Rich people were happy to pay large sums for the truly magnificent work of these skilled engravers. More and more families came over and set up business here and by 1850-1860, England was producing most of the finest glass engravings in Europe.

There is no better way to determine quality in an item than by handling it. Look for imperfections and if possible an indication as to when it was made. Examine any engraving; check for damage on the rim and feet and question whether the weight of the glass feels right. Examine the underside of the glass with a x10 magnifier and look for scratches. Be cautious - sometimes scratches are added to simulate age.

Victorian glass rummer, 6" high, circa 1840
inscribed with Masonic engravings all around.
Marked Sutherland Lodge 451. 'Frangas Non
Electes'. Estimate: £200-250 ($300-375)

It is usual, after having performed the Masonic ritual in the Temple, that the brethren celebrated their day with a dinner, fine wine, speeches and toasts. To assist them in this tradition they used, and sometimes still do, a 'Firing glass'. This is a short, 'dumpy' glass with a very heavy base. It was used to rhythmically bang on the table to mimic gunfire, as an accolade to a toast. These are usually made of clear glass, and some are beautifully decorated in gold lacquer with the square and compasses engraved on them. Naturally, in the merriment of the evening, many were broken, so numbers are few. The average price for a 19th century engraved firing glass is about £45-95. They are worth collecting for the future.

Most Masonic glass collectables are rising fast in value and more and more are being collected by museums and other establishments. Some pieces are being taken abroad, especially to America. In America you can buy most things with a Masonic logo on, from key rings to car number plates. Even bed sheets, counterpanes and pillows can be bought with Masonic logos on. However the United States do not have the variety and

Fakes and Copies

One can well imagine with the prices shown for Masonic collectables in this book, someone is going to try their hand at producing reproductions and fakes. It can be a lucrative business. In the past they were very prolific and actually advertised their craft of copying and faking. Today I suppose we would call it reproduction, but when it is produced to deceive for profit, this becomes a crime and a nuisance.

You will need a very discerning eye to detect these fakes as manufacturers become more and more skilled. Again, it is experience that counts because the more of the genuine article that you handle, the better chance you have of detecting a fake.

Early drinking glasses faked to order have been commercially available from the early 20th century. Indeed, one could order Georgian and Jacobean glasses and decanters from a catalogue, and I am sorry to say they would include Masonic designs on them to order.

A famous antique dealer, Mrs. Graydon-Stannus, prided herself in deceiving glass collectors with her fakes; she produced some fine glass engravings, shown in her book Old Irish Glass. She deliberately cut and engraved well-known pieces to boost their value. She came from the Waterford line of famous glassmakers. One of her best customers died in 1936 and his dependents received a great shock, when the auction of his collection, expected to fetch £13,000, only made £900, as most of the pieces were fakes.

How can the poor collector tell the difference? It's not easy, especially when many genuine dealers can be caught out. The modern fakes are usually beautifully made, in most cases better than the originals. Older glass, particularly 18th century, carries with it certain characteristics, which are difficult to reproduce. There was a bluish colour to it. It was heavier, thicker and had more air bubbles than new pieces. There was a deliberate attempt at faking in as much that the sharp cut-off point or 'pontil' that one usually associates with a hand blown piece of glass was even copied. In fact it was often requested by customers that this should be a feature of their reproduction glassware.

When paying high prices you have to trust your dealer. If he has unfortunately made a mistake, then he would have to honour your receipt and repay your money as long as the goods were not marked as seen or as found.

quantity of antique Masonic pieces as we do in the UK. As a result, Americans are very interested in British Masonic collectables and this consequently pushes up prices in this country.

Artistically engraved decanters and wine glasses, punch bowls and a good selection of Masonic glass in Bristol Blue are very collectable. These are still available, but be prepared to travel to auctions far afield to find them. Today, unfortunately, these magnificent specimens of an engraver's art are no longer made, or if they are they are few and far between. Many of the great artists are gone and the cost today would be very expensive to make in the numbers they were made 200 years ago.

The tall, chunky, Victorian rummers that hold nearly a pint for swilling down great gobfulls of wine are also very interesting, engraved usually with an ordinary square and compasses but sometimes more elaborate if intended as a gift. One of these could cost around £250-300 ($375-450). There are still quite a number available. I paid £750 ($1,125) for a large two pint glass with

Masonic markings and a small family tree dating back to 1780. There is a hollow bulb in the stem of the glass, and the glassmaker had inserted a Groat coin which rattles when you shake the glass. Unfortunately, over the years the coin has etched the glass from the inside and the coin and its date has become obscured.

Single glass from a boxed set of six, the box with some damage. Estimate: £10-15 ($15-22) for single glass.

*Large two-pint glass, 10"
high, presentation rummer on
a circular pedestal. Engraved
around the outside with
Masonic symbols of the
Ancients Freemasons, and also
engraved with the names of a
family showing their dates of
birth, back to 1784.
Estimate: £750-850
($1,125-1,275)*

*Bristol blue Firing glass,
modern engraved millennium
2000 limited edition.
Estimate: £50-60 ($75-95)*

*An unusual eight-sided,
engraved clear
Bohemian drinking
glass, 7" high.
Estimate: £175-225
($262-337)*

*Watch out for modern Bohemian Glass from the
continent. It looks very smart but on close inspection
and by asking leading questions one will find that it is
21st Century.*

*Three turn of the 18th century Masonic glasses very
well engraved. Estimates: Mid £175-225 $262-337.
Left & Right £95-120 ($142-180) each.*

*This picture shows the boxed set of
glasses. Estimate: £60-90 ($90-135)*

A very fine late Georgian punch bowl complete with original ladle. Engraved all around outside with Masonic Ancients' emblems. Estimate: £800-900 ($1,200-1,350)

Wine glass.

Firing glass.

Wine goblet.

A selection of beautifully engraved glasses, the property of Poole Masonic Museum. The estimated value of these glasses range from £300-450 ($450-675) each, depending on size and complexity of the designs.

WATCHES

Mr C. Clark Julius of Philadelphia, USA has amassed a very large collection of Masonic items, possibly one of the largest in America. He has written several books on the subject, but unfortunately most of the items listed in his book will not be found in the UK, having been made in America for native Freemasons. He has kindly allowed me to use information from his books to tell you about Masonic watches. The oldest Masonic watch in his collection is a pocket watch by Burtenshaw Aldgate and was made in London in 1768. It has a white face decorated with Masonic figures and a verge movement. He claims that it is the oldest Masonic watch ever manufactured.

Silver pocket watch with a dial showing Masonic emblems. The watch is circa 1900 by H.Samuel. There were hundreds of different Masonic watches made. They are very collectable, scarce and expensive. Beware many of them are not authentic and there are many copies on the market. Estimate: £225-275 ($330-400)

The Swiss made many Masonic watches. One of them, a travel clock, had the Masonic symbols placed on the face to represent the hours of the day. In a 4" square leather case, when the lever on the side is pushed it rings the hour and chimes the minutes. This watch is very rare. The Swiss were also responsible for making the Triangular watch late in the

An unusual gold Triangle pocket watch with various Masonic logos replacing the figures within the face. Estimate: £1,800-2,000 ($2,700-3,000)

1800s. They actually made three different patterned cases. They were in gold and measured 2.5" across the base and equilateral sides and 3/8" thick. The first watch has a round dial with Masonic emblems replacing numerals, with a large letter 'G' at the top of the case and a large 'J' at the bottom with a 'B' on both sides at the front. These letters stand for Jachin and Boaz, which are the 2 pillars at the porchway or entrance of King Solomon's Temple. The 'G' stands for Geometric/Geometry. Interestingly, in 1730, the Premier Grand Lodge of England became concerned at the number of imposters who were passing themselves off as Freemasons and in an endeavour to trap them, they changed these letters around. It was assumed that any true Mason would only use a watch on which he knew the correct letter layout. It reverted to normal when the lodges amalgamated in 1813, although some never bothered to change back. To a collector these would be worth several hundred pounds.

After 1900, the American market could see the demand for these Masonic watches and companies in America such as Elgin, Hamilton and Waltham all started making them in various designs and materials. The ornamented dials and cases became more and more personal as watches became tailor-made.

The most sought-after of all is the Dudley watch, made for a Mason by a Mason. William Wallace Dudley was the maker. He was born in 1851 in New Brunswick, Canada. He became interested in watches and horology at the age of 13, when he began an apprenticeship making ship chronometers in Canada. When he moved to America he worked for two watch companies, firstly The Trenton Watch Co., before going on to the Hamilton Watch Co. in Lancaster. He left them at the age of 69 to start his own Company. His first watches were produced in 1922; they were 14S, 19J, and used Waltham Model 1894 -1897, 14 size parts including train and escapement. The plates and winding mechanism were made at the Dudley plant. Dials and hands were made to Dudley's specifications in Switzerland. On some of his watches the face had no Masonic symbol but Masonic emblems could be found inside the working parts of the watch. The actual symbols were a slipper, plumb rule, trowel, level square, compasses, the bible and the letter 'G'. This was truly fine engineering. Unfortunately, over the years and despite their range, the Dudley Company sunk into decline and on February 20th 1925 William filed for a petition for bankruptcy. Dudley died in 1938 having made 2,600 watches. Of these, only 135 were actually sold. They are now very scarce and very collectable.

Dudley No. 1 Model
Bible is part of the bridge work.

Dudley No. 2 Model
Bible is a silver coloured mounted as is screws the level plates

Dudley No. 3 Model
Only difference the Silver bible is riveted on and the Level is rounded on the top.

Model No.1, 14S, 19J, Open Face, can be distinguished by the Holy Bible engraved on the winding arbor plate, and a gilded pallet bridge matching the plates. Estimated production from 1920 to 1925 = 1,400 Serial nos. 500 to 1900. 14S Dudley, 19J. 14 karat, Flip open back, Serial No.1. 5 experimental models were made, and can fetch £10,000 ($14,200) in mint condition. 14S. M. No.1. 19J. Open Face, 14 Karat, Flip open back, £3,250 ($4,615) With box and papers, £3,500 ($5,000) In good condition.

Model No.2, 12S, 19J, used the 910 and 912 Hamilton wheels and escapement, and has a flat silver-coloured Bible. Estimated production from 1925 to 1935 = 2,800. Serial nos. 2001 to 4800. Model No.2. Three types can fetch between £2,250-2,600 ($3,200-3,700).

Model No.3, 12S, can be distinguished by the silver Bible which was riveted in place and was three-dimensional. The 3rd wheel bridge was rounded off at one end. Estimated production from 1935 to 1976 = 1,700. Serial nos. 4801 to 6500. Model No.3. Fetches between £2,250-2,600 ($3,200-3,700).

This triangular shape were made by many different watch manufacturers including Rolex.

There were a few of the Triangular pocket watches made by various companies, most being with Masonic logos. Masonic Triangular watch, Swiss, 17J, mother of pearl, 1920s, in good condition Estimate: £1,100-1,300 ($1,700-2,000). As above with blue stone in crown, 1905, in good condition Estimate: £1,300-2,000 ($2,000-3,000)

Pocket watch with Masonic logos on the face. Estimate: £1,000-1,200 ($1,500-1,800)

Pocket Hunter watch solid gold with Masonic logo Square and Compass on the face. Estimate: £1,500-1,700 ($1,500-1,800)

Masonic presentation clock made in Germany, maker unknown. Estimate: £1,500-1,800 ($2,250-2,700)

18 carat gold pocket watch with Masonic logo on the face, Estimate: £900-1,000 ($1,350-1,500)

These items illustrated above were by kind permission of Poole Masonic Museum. The exact prices paid for them are unknown and many of them were free gifts to the Museum. The estimates are as shown.

BOOKS

Masonic books, many of them illustrated, are available in good second-hand bookshops in abundance. There were literally thousands printed over the years, many leather-bound with exquisite colour plates. One can still purchase books with prints showing the wearing of Masonic regalia in humourous caricatures of the day. There is no undocumented subject in Freemasonry. The secret rituals that Masons use are now available to the public in book form - hardly a secret anymore. And today, people are still writing books and revealing new facts about Freemasonry. It is a fascinating subject and has occupied the waking hours of many a learned scholar. Because there are so many books out there and they are so easy to buy, it is possible that a new collector may choose to specialise in this field. A book should cost between £5-50 and a set obviously more. One of the best authors of such books is R.F. Gould.

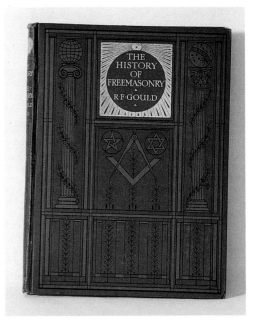

Masonic books in good condition retain their value and increase as time goes by. A second-hand set of six volumes titled *The History of Freemasonry* by R.F. Gould sold for £100 ($150) recently. New books on Freemasonry are being written all the time, but it is the older books with histories of lodge meetings during the 18th century that are more collectable. They document the atmosphere and background of the pubs and how they dined and the prices the locals paid for their food and beer. There are also books on lodges in foreign countries and their records. Many books

A single copy of a set of six books by R.F. Gould fully illustrated.

The complete set of six is estimated at £90-100 ($140-150)

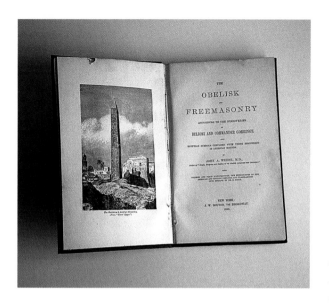

Book, circa 1810 of the History of the Obelisks of Egypt and their links with Freemasonry.
Estimate: £20-25 ($30-40)

written were on the duties of the master and his wardens. How they were to behave and run the lodge, the fees charged and what uses the funds were put to. Also, there are many books dealing with regalia of all the different degrees and splinter groups of lodges within the boundaries of the Grand Lodge of England.

As well as the books written in English on English lodges, there are a similar number written on lodges abroad; France, Germany, Ireland, America and all over the middle and far east. Nearly every country has written records of their lodges. There is even a lodge in Katmandu, high up in the mountains of Nepal.

Who's who in Freemasonry? It's all catalogued; the great men of the past, with a short history of their past and qualifications. Books on making after-dinner speaking, Masonic jokes, Freemasonry and the Church. There are so many titles to choose from and so many different sizes and types of books, it really is a collector's paradise to specialise in.

The story of Grand Lodge.
Estimate: £18-20 ($27-30)

PRINTS AND PAINTINGS

Masonic SPY prints published by Vanity Fair 13th June, 1898. 14 of these prints were produced of famous Freemasons. Each one was accompanied by a short introduction to the person and his achievements. Worth about £40 each. Only 3 of the set show the Masons in Masonic regalia. All the prices for these prints are given as unframed.

Spy print The Worshipful Grand Master, a caricature of him in regalia printed 1869. Very collectable. Individually, its value is twice that of the others.

Vanity Fair print by Spy, The Grand Secretary, in regalia.

Vanity Fair print. The Provincial Grand Master in regalia Earl Amhurst, printed 1904.

The Lord Mayor of London, Sir Joseph Cockfield Dimsdale; Bart, MP, J.P and other things (unquote). Spy print from Vanity Fair.

These four prints have an estimated value of £40-50 ($60-75) each.

WHAT TO LOOK FOR

New Lord Mayor, Sir Henry Aaron Isaacs, A Freemason. Vanity Fair. 1889.

Vanity Fair was a weekly magazine published between 1868-1914 and sold at one shilling (5p). It tended to reflect the views of those in more affluent positions. In its issue on the 13th June 1869, it printed a coloured lithograph caricature of Benjamin Disraeli, drawn by Carlo Pellgrini who used the signature 'Ape'. From those beginnings were born the Vanity Fair Prints.

Famous caricaturist Max Beerbolm was a Vanity Fair artist and Sir Leslie Ward used the signature 'Spy'. It is little known but several other artists such as Tissot, Sickert and Whistler also contributed to Vanity Fair.

These prints come up at auctions on many occasions in a wide range of characters. Masonic prints are particularly collectable, although, Cricketers, Jockeys, Rowers, Foxhunters, Judges and Politicians are all popular.

Most of these prints sell for around £40-70 ($60-105), although many will fetch more than £100 ($150). It is the sportsmen and judges which are particularly collectable, the rarest Cricketer is E.W. Dillon estimated at £2,000 ($3,000).

Beware, there are many reproductions of these prints, especially the more expensive ones.

During the mid 19th century, *Vanity Fair Magazine* published a series of well-known lords and gentry who were Masons, some of whom shown in their full Masonic regalia. These prints were well publicised and welcomed by Victorian readers. Several different artists painted them: SPY, APE, and AST, pseudonyms of the artists who designed or

NIGHT.

painted them. They were announced in the paper in advance and interested customers ordered them. They came complete with a short history of the man's life and his achievements.

Most of these gentlemen were Lords, Knights of the Realm and dignitaries of great standing, such as The Lord Mayor of London. However, there were also four non-titled men amongst them. Four of the prints are caricature pictures of them wearing their full regalia, not drawn to ridicule them, but to emphasise their finer points. A set of fourteen such caricature pictures costs about £400 unframed and interestingly there is a collectors' club in Bournemouth for collectors of *Vanity Fair* prints.

The *Illustrated London News* also published many fine pictures, one of which being the procession of Masons, all wearing top hats and full regalia, as they paraded through the city of Plymouth on their way to see the Grand Master, The Prince of Wales, in 1874. Another picture depicts the installation of The Prince of Wales on 8th May, 1875.

Perhaps the most famous print is from a set of four originally drawn by William Hogarth (1697-1764), a prolific painter and printer of great renown. His works were always in great demand throughout his life and many artists copied his work. Most of the plates of his prints were destroyed in the First World War, when they were melted down and used for the war effort, although all his work is catalogued. This particular set of four prints named 'Four times of the day' shows typical and topical scenes of London, each a scene from a different time of day. They are Morning, Noon, Evening and Night. It is the latter which is most sought-after and is the only one depicting a Masonic scene. As they are normally sold as a set, it is hard to buy this picture on its own. The price for a genuine set is £400 ($600) upwards, depending on condition. In this Mason's print is Sir Thomas de Ville, a Bow Street magistrate, who is renowned for scorning those who come before him in the dock for drink-related charges. Here he is, obviously the worse for wear himself, being helped home at night by a lady through a crowded London street and as they pass under an open window someone empties the contents of a chamber pot over his head. He was a most reviled man it seems, even before the soaking.

Boxed set of silver Masonic tea spoons with enamelled heads. Estimate: £60-75 ($90-112)

Set of minature ivory hand carved working tools in a blue case. circa 20th century. Estimate: £120-150 ($180-225)

MISCELLANEOUS COLLECTABLES

Silver plated American matchbox. Very collectable and scarce. Embossed on both sides with Masonic emblems, circa 1900. Estimate: £60-100 ($90-150)

As mentioned previously, the USA has an abundance of different Masonic goodies - so many that some find their way over here to the UK. Naturally, they have their own collectors and in fact that's where a lot of our pieces are sold. I have found three books devoted mainly to American Masonic collectables, but the contents sometimes have English items in them. They make interesting reading and show the scope open to the small collector with a limited budget. The author of these is C. Clark Julius and he welcomes you to correspond with him as a collector. His books are listed under Recommended Reading at the rear of the book.

Leather jewel pouch in good conditon with key.
Estimate: £25-35 ($37-50)

A brass flat iron stand. Parts of
the stand have been cut out to
represent Masonic symbols.
Estimate: £60-90 ($90-135)

Tortoiseshell trinket box with silver Masonic engraved
plate on lid. Estimate: £200-250 ($300-375)

Inlaid glove box with
Masonic emblems.
Estimate: £150-200 ($225-300)

Rare silver locket jewel
R.M.B.I. Estimate: £80-150
($120-225)

Set of Masonic playing cards with reverse printed with Masonic emblems. Estimate: £20-30 ($30-45)

Postcard of Don Bradman, the great Australian batsman & Captain who was a Freemason. Estimate: £150-175 ($225-260)

Engraved marble Masonic Temple stone 'Smooth Ashler'. Estimate: £750-1,000 ($1,125-1,500)

A collection of gavels of various materials including wood, ivory and bone.

Examples: *Ivory pieces fetch £200-300 ($300-450)*

                Bone pieces fetch £80-120 ($120-180)

                Wooden pieces fetch £60-80 ($90-120)

Masonic Silver Coffee pot.
Estimate: £1,500-2,000 ($2,250-3,000)

Silver Masonic buckle.
Estimate: £100-150 ($150-225)

Old brass Masonic buckle c.1910.
Estimate: £60-80 ($90-120)

Silver Masonic pen knife.
Estimate: £35-45 ($53-68)

Old stoneware maul.
Estimate: £200-250 ($300-375)

BAROMETERS

I expect many older collectors remember their grandparents tapping the glass of a long, wooden banjo-like object, hanging in the hallway of their home to see if the needle inside would move to indicate a dry day. These mercury barometers work on the air

PRICES FOR BAROMETERS

Initially barometers were made purely as scientific instruments, but by about 1680 they were produced for domestic use, and although a number were made to determine altitude and give accurate air pressure readings, the vast majority were seen as domestic wall fittings and were subject to similar stylistic changes and influences.

Mercury barometers come in two catagories, 'stick' and 'wheel'. Stick barometers display the mercury column enabling it to be read directly against the register plate, which up to the mid-19th century were usually made of brass. From about 1840, ivory and bone were mainly used for register plates.

Wheel barometers, sometimes known as 'Banjo", use a simple pully mechanism which allows a reading to be made on a dial which is generally circular and of silvered brass.

The aneroid barometer was invented around 1843, using an evacuated sealed chamber instead of mercury to measure air pressure.

Prices for barometers are currently holding their own. Generally, prices are determined by quality; less expensive stick barometers fetch between £300-700 ($450-1,050) whilst the top end of the range like a bowfront 'stick' can fetch four figures; between £5,500-£8,000 ($8,250-12,000). 'Stick' are in far greater demand than 'wheel' barometers. A late 19th century mediocre wheel barometer is estimated between £150-250 ($225-375). Early 19th century examples fetch between £500-1,500 ($750-2,750), but many 18th century wheel barometers can make up to £4,000 ($6,000) and more. Aneroid barometers sell in the trade between £60-250 ($90-375) although some good examples can go for more than £500 ($750).

Masonic emblems on a barometer can be expected to fetch the value up to between 15 to 20 per cent and maybe more according to demand.

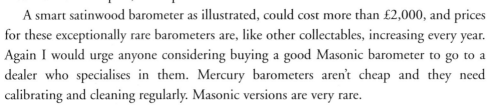

Very unusual satinwood mercury banjo-type barometer circa 1820, made for a Masonic customer by the famous Italian manufacturer Schalfino of Taunton. It has a silvered dial cast brass rim and Masonic logo in the centre. Estimate: £2,000-2,200 ($3,000-3,300)

pressure bearing down on the surface of some mercury in a glass tube. This movement is recorded and displayed on a dial or, in the case of stick barometers, with longitude movement by a pointer. These barometers were often made to order and adorned with the name of the maker and the client's name or business and, if required, Masonic emblems.

The mercury barometer was made up until 1860 when the aneroid barometer, which worked on the principle of expanding and contracting metal bellows, meant a more compact, less expensive barometer.

A smart satinwood barometer as illustrated, could cost more than £2,000, and prices for these exceptionally rare barometers are, like other collectables, increasing every year. Again I would urge anyone considering buying a good Masonic barometer to go to a dealer who specialises in them. Mercury barometers aren't cheap and they need calibrating and cleaning regularly. Masonic versions are very rare.

One must take care with mercury filled barometers. Over the years the glass tube filled with mercury ages, also the fine cord which operates the needle becomes fragile. It is therefore important that the barometer has been thoroughly overhauled by a specialist with a certificate to that effect.

It is expensive to service a neglected mercury barometer and should be carried out by a barometer specialist.

Never lay a mercury filled barometer on its back or side. It must be kept upright at all times. The glass tube should be plugged when in transit.

GRANDFATHER CLOCKS

Among the unusual items engraved with Masonic logos, are grandfather clocks. From the beginning of the 18th to the end of the 19th century, the gentry of England took pride in the fact that they were Freemasons and made sure that visitors to their houses and their families were made aware of it. They achieved this by proudly displaying their grand eye-catching pieces of furniture such as grandfather clocks and barometers in prominent places such as

Grandfather clock, eight day chiming every quarter, with Masonic logos. Estimate: £3,000-4,500 ($4,500-4,700)

the hallway or the lounge. The pieces were decorated with Masonic logos so that it was clear what they represented.

There was a magnificent early 19th century wooden tea caddy covered in Masonic logos on sale at the NEC Birmingham in 2001, not overpriced for such a rare item at over £4,000. Even everyday items like tea caddies would receive the Masonic treatment. These clocks were made to order. Very few exist today in their original cases.

POINTS TO LOOK FOR

With or without a Masonic emblem, a clock needs to be in good condition to start with, especially longcase clocks, which is the proper name for Grandfather clocks. But, all things being equal, the Masonic emblems will add to the value of a good clock and sometimes very considerably.

Buying longcase clocks can be a tricky business and it is probably best if you buy from an established dealer who would give you a guarantee to its condition and provenence. When contemplating a purchase, bear in mind the possibility of the movement and the case being a marriage. This is acceptable providing the two are contemporary and they haven't been altered to fit each other. Some renovation to the case is to be expected, expecially the repair of the plinth. Many stood on damp stone floors which were frequently washed and the wood eventually rotted in parts.

Be especially cautious when looking at dials, particularly painted ones. A good maker's name might have been added. Brass dials can be reproductions that have been deliberately distressed, which would be obvious to an expert but an amateur may be taken in by the deception.

The most important part of any clock is the movement. The fact that a clock ticks for a few minutes in a saleroom is no guarantee that it is in good order. Check that the striking is correct by moving the minute hand slowly clockwise, allowing each hour to strike, in particular make sure that it strikes in order at eleven, twelve and one.

Clocks may appear to be better than they actually are in auction rooms to the layman, where it may seem that the purchase is good. To find out later that an excessive restoration has been made can be a costly mistake. However, it may be acceptable to buy a clock in need of repair if it is cheap, but make sure it can be repaired before buying it. If you would prefer to buy at auction, an established auction house is the best place to go, and if you have a valuable clock to sell it is wise to get a professional valuation before submitting to a reputable auctioneer.

SMALLER COLLECTABLE ITEMS

Lapel pins

There are thousands of different lapel pins to collect. Each year the brethren between themselves have manufactured a lapel pin to show off their own particular circle of Lodge Masters for that year, of which they are immensely proud. There is a great assortment of these to be found. Rummage round in the oddment boxes at fleamarkets; they are very small and can go unnoticed. Most people wouldn't know the relevance of them. Price from 50p each.

Bowling Club badges

Every county in England had or has a Masonic bowling club, and most of these have an enamelled lapel brooch to show off their team. These are very attractive and show a big variety of individual bowling club designs. Again, you will often find these in boxes of odds and ends at fleamarkets and fairs. They make fine collections. Price 50p upwards - inexpensive and could be worth collecting for the future.

Ties

It has been customary up to quite recently that only black ties or bows could be worn in the lodge, which in the first place was in respect for those men and women who fell in the Great War of 1914-18. Colour is now being introduced and various counties are designing ties for their different provinces showing perhaps, the local county crest and Masonic symbols.

I doubt whether the day will come when Freemasons will attend their lodges in jeans and T-shirts, but they are now allowed to wear ties during their time outside the lodge, showing quite clearly that they are Freemasons.

The ties come in all types of designs. More Masons are seen in public wearing them and you can be sure that many more decorative Masonic ties will come onto the market in the future. This can be an interesting area to collect in and perhaps a collectable for the future.

Sometimes ties are issued to aid fundraising and may show a Masonic logo and perhaps the date of the fund. These ties can be worn in the Lodge or outside. These ties are available from Lodge Secretaries and regalia shops which specialise in Masonic regalia.

Masonic Jewellery and Rings

Masons have worn rings and tie pins since the brotherhood began. Most of them are made of precious metal and some with stones. Prices start at about £200 for both the tie pin and a smart ring. It pays to shop around at the antique fairs. In 1997 I bought a very old 18 karat 12.5 gram gold signet ring, beautifully engraved with the Masonic logo. The gold had worn on the edges but the ring cost me just £60 - a very good price for a ring of that weight, even without the Masonic logo.

The ladies have not been overlooked through the ages. There are now Masonic Lodges for women that operate in a very similar fashion to that of the men's. They have their own jewels and regalia, and these appear on the market from time to time, but are fewer in numbers. Apart from the regalia and jewels of the Lady Lodges, a fair amount of jewellery was manufactured for the wives of Freemasons including watches, brooches, rings and other assorted pieces with the Square and Compasses logo.

This is a 9ct watch fob donated to Marine Lodge. The fob has the name of the lodge on it, circa 1910. Estimate: £70-80 ($100-120)

Masonic square gold cube, very unusual, also shown in the open out position. These usually appear as a round ball, ranging from 6mm to 30 mm in size. There are 4 different ones to collect. The value of each will depend on the gold content, the size and the age of the ball.
The cube and other shapes are more valuable than the ball.
Estimate: Cube £150-250 ($225-375)
Ball £100-150 ($150-220)

Masonic Balls

There are balls, made of gold or gold outside and silver inside, which open out to display a cross or crucifix. On each face of the segments making up the ball is engraved a Masonic symbol. Although no-one is certain how these balls originated, they were probably manufactured at the beginning of the 20th century. There are, it seems, four different types - English, Scottish, German and an older type of English. You can find them in the shops but the older ones are more collectable and scarce. On the modern English models you will find a small knob which, when depressed, releases the ball from its housing. The older models are held together by indentations in the claws surrounding the ball. They are available in various sizes from under 1/4" to 1" in diameter and are usually worn round the neck by ladies or on a man's key chain. Some of the older balls are quite rare, but you will have to pay over £100 for a modern one in a shop. A really old one would cost between £200-300 ($300-450) but these are very rare.

THE WORK OF BROTHER C. CLARK JULIUS

I send Brother C. Clark Julius my grateful thanks and appreciation for allowing me to include some of his work below in this book and my admiration for a lifetime dedicated in collecting and recording Masonic collectables.

I would rate him as one of the finest authorities on collecting Masonic items in the world. He has amassed a tremendous collection. He has documented the history of his collection, and in future when this hobby becomes more widespread, these references will be respected as the impressive results of a man's lifetime dedication to his hobby. Here is a small sample of his collection.

A. German
The German ball has the same characteristic as the Scottish and English ball, with one difference, the outside claws that hold the ball together is of a larger and more robust type. Date back of 1900 and manufactured in Germany.

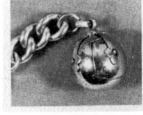

Blue — Chapter Knife

Knights Templar Knife

This is a Tiffany-Swiss watch, 17-jeweled, gold case, very thin, No. 10 size, porcelain dial with Roman numerals, square and compass with a "G" on left side, Knights Templar Cross and Crown on the right. Made for Tiffany's Jewelery Company of New York City.

Tiffany's watch

This is a Tiffany-Swiss watch, 17-jeweled, gold case, very thin, No. 10 size, porcelain dial with Roman numerals, square and compass with a "G" on left side, Knights Templar Cross and Crown on the right. Made for Tiffany's Jewelery Company of New York City.

This a Tavannes watch, oval case, pink gold with gold face which has Masonic emblems as numerals, 15-jeweled Swiss movement made for Longine Company; circa 1914-1916. This watch was made to be sold in Germany.

Tavannes Watch

CARING FOR YOUR COLLECTION

As you can see by some of the high prices mentioned in this book and the accumulative value of a collection, it would be folly not to have them insured. This need not prove expensive. When I contacted my insurance company about my collection I was told that it was covered under my comprehensive house contents policy. I have still taken other precautions to safeguard against theft, and each item is catalogued and photographed.

Be very careful when cleaning lustreware pottery items. Do not use water and detergent or you will remove the delicate lustre finish. At most, wipe over with tepid water. Remember these are very old and time-aged pieces and modern detergents can be too strong for the delicate designs.

When you display plates, avoid hanging them on wire stretchers as they can chip the edges. There is a comprehensive range of stands available for displaying plates, cups and bowls and there are retailers who specialise in these items.

Sunlight has a bad effect on materials and the paintwork on Sunderland Lustreware. Be sure to keep your collection away from direct heat, fires and radiators. If you don't, cracks will soon appear. You may be able to repair a chip on your china but a crack is quite a problem.

I couldn't believe my eyes when I recently saw a Montague Dawson print for sale at the price of £150. It was a big picture of a smuggling scene and the picture gave the impression of pale moonlight. There was a little bit of light peeking through from a milky moon and the picture looked perfectly all right. I bought it and took it to an art dealer expecting to at least double my outlay, only to be told 'it was faded by sunlight'. I was lucky - I managed to get my money back.

Don't let admirers handle your collection with dirty hands. I went to the Masonic Museum in Great Queen Street a few months ago to discuss the writing of this book with the curator, a Mr. Mark Dennis. In his office he had a brass iron stand. He put on a pair of white gloves to pick it up and show me, pointing out that you should never handle antiques with uncovered hands as the acidic perspiration can corrode pieces over time.

It is a good idea to gently wind an old watch or clock occasionally; just a few turns so as to keep the workings from seizing up. Be careful not to over-wind.

Your collection of jewels may have tatty dirty ribbons and broken pins because you have been unable to afford better replacements. These can be repaired. Try the Museum in Poole. They repair jewels and I expect that most retailers will know of a firm that specialises in the renovation of regalia and jewels.

A word of caution (All that looks Masonic- ain't!)

When you start to collect Masonic collectables, be aware that the very famous brotherhood of Oddfellows which also dates back hundreds of years, use very similar symbols as Freemasonry. They use the square and compasses, the letter 'G' in the centre, the 'all-seeing eye' and they also use their own symbols including a hand with a heart in the centre, the open book, an arm with an axe, a sand dial, floral displays and angels. It is very easy for a novice collector to make the mistake of confusing the two. I have known dealers who have tried to sell me an Oddfellow's jug, believing it to be Masonic. There are other brotherhoods and friendly societies with similar emblems, so be on your guard. This is an easy mistake when buying lustreware because both brotherhoods who closely operated together centuries ago before they went their separate ways, ordered vast quantities of jugs, plates and bowls with their independent but similar logos on, from the same manufacturers and mistakes were sometimes made when goods were sent to the wrong groups.

Masonic collectables are holding their price very well, and can only increase. It is a good investment.

BUYING AT AUCTION

There is a good chance of picking up a nice piece of glass, china or other collectable at a reasonable price at antiques fairs, but it is in the auction houses that one would have more chance to find the quality pieces.

If you find an auction with a Masonic item for sale, don't take the auctioneer's word for its condition or age. Having read the catalogues ask to see and examine it with the eagle eye of a professional. Nitpick if necessary. Is it a fake? Has it been expertly restored? It is your decision, so acquire as much information as you can. Ask a few questions of the auction house specialist. Where has the item come from? Has it been in auction before? If so, what sort of price was offered? Did it reach its reserve?

Once you have decided that the article is to your liking, you will have to decide the ceiling price that you are going to bid to. Let's imagine it is a Creamware jug, circa 1800, with minor foot rim chips. Check that the Masonic black painted artwork or transfer prints have not faded. It is to all appearances a very nice jug. It is sometimes worth tapping lightly against the side of a jug to see if it gives a clear ring and not a dull one, which usually reveals a cleverly concealed crack. If you could buy a perfect jug for £1,600 you would have a bargain. The catalogue reads an estimate of £1,000-1,200. Perhaps in the unlikely event that no other bidder is interested, then as the only person there you might be lucky and bag it for £1,000.

So having decided that your limit is, say, £1,700, don't spend a penny more. Consider the auction house commission which is at least 15% of the hammer price, and the VAT on the commission price, plus insurance. So now one is looking at 20% on top of the bid price. This also applies if you are selling an item. If your item sells at its reserve, you can expect 20-25% less when you receive your cheque. Now, your £1,700 is now looking more like £1,900.

Having made the final bid and also having had your cheque cleared with the auction house, go to the collection point to collect your buy. Examine the piece once more in great detail. Remember, many others have handled that item since you last inspected it, and they may not all have been as kind with it as you. Make sure it is in exactly the same condition as when you last examined it.

Recently I bought a box of mixed Masonic items in a case and on collecting them I declined the sensible offer by the lady controlling the counter to inspect the goods. On inspecting them later I found that all the choice items had been stolen and I was left with all the junk. The Auctioneers were very sympathetic, but there was nothing they could or would do, as I had signed my right away and especially as I had already been invited to check my purchase and declined the offer.

Masonic Collectable Auction held at Bonhams, Leeds

Bonhams Auctioneers and Valuers held a Masonic Collectables auction on Wednesday, 12th June, 2002 at their Leeds saleroom. Our special thanks to Matthew Coles (Specialist Masonica) of Bonhams for supplying the results and pictures from this auction.

Although the prices of lots can differ from auction to auction, the hammer prices are as near as one can accept when making a reasonable valuation, and this book has considered this fact within the estimates given. Readers should also note that auctioneers today add a buyers premium on which the buyer also pays VAT. This particular Bonhams auctions carries a premium of 17.5% plus VAT, so in calculating a bid price, 20.56% should also be added. ie. Lot 385 Triangular Watch, winning bid of £1,550.00 plus 20.56%; the buyer would actually pay £1,868.68.

In the Jewellery and Watches section there were 10 lots and most exceeded estimates, with the highest going to lot 385, a Swiss Triangular watch, fetching £1,550.

Jewels section held 33 lots Most of these fetched less than estimates. However, lot 410 was interesting, a Martin Foulkes medal cast with a portrait of Martin Foulkes, the reverse with sphinx with crescent moon on its flank, a pyramid between two columns, the sun at its meridian. Sold for £300 ($450). (Only ten examples are believed to exist, of which several are in museums).

Ceramics and Glass section was good with 31 lots, most fetching more than estimates. Lot 426, a set of 14 early 19th century blue & white transfer printed bowls and five side plates, most cracked. Sold for £800 ($1,200).

Books section consisted of 19 lots all fetching reasonable prices, the top lot being No. 457 'The Masonic Record', Vols. 1-17 (1920-37) and Vols. 21-24 (1940-44), clothbound fetched £200 ($300).

Miscellaneous section with 19 lots, all interesting and most topping their estimates. Lot 476 being an album of Masonic first-day covers fetching £550 ($775).

The highest price paid was for lot 488, an early oak throne. The plaque on the back was inscribed 'This chair is made of the old oak and bell metal of York Minster destroyed by fire May 20th 1840'.
Estimated £1,000-1,500 ($1,500-2,250)
Sold for £3,300 ($4,950)

The second highest price paid was for lot 385, a Swiss silver keyless pocket watch. The triangular case was decorated in relief, the mother of pearl dial with coloured symbols and the inscription 'Love your fellow man lend him a helping hand'. Import marks for 1925, in original card box with spare glass.
Estimated £1,000-1,500 ($1,500-2,250)
Sold for £1,550 ($2,325)

Selection of lots from the Ceramics and Glass section

Top row from left to right: Lot 423, *early 19th century drinking glass with engraved Masonic symbols and inscribed Lodge No. 199, 13cm high.*
Estimated £150-200 ($225-300). Sold for £230 ($345)

Lot 420, *early 19th century firing glass with Masonic symbols, 15cm high, plus another firing glass with octagonal tapering foot. 14cm high.*
Estimated £200-300 ($300-450). Sold for £320 ($480) the pair.

Lot 424, *Bohemian red firing glass, engraved with a chair under a canopy surrounded by symbols similar to Masonry, inscribed August Freiedrich Ahlers, 12cm high.*
Estimated £60-80 ($90-120). Sold for £95 ($142.50)

Bottom row left to right: Lot 444, *Milchglass mug, painted with flowers and a panel of Masonic symbols, 10cm high. Estimated £80-120 ($120-180). Sold for £190 ($285).*

Lot 440, *Sunderland lustre jug with view of cast iron bridge and Masonic symbols and a poem celebrating the return of a ship, all hand-coloured. 24cm high.*
Estimated £300-500 ($450-750). Sold for £520 ($780)

Lot 442, *19th century earthenware jug, printed with flowers and a gentleman seated by the arms of the Premier Grand Lodge with the inscription 'Industry, Providence, Love & Truth, The Freemasons Arms'.*
Estimated £120-180 ($180-270). Sold for £240 ($360)